THE ADMINISTRATION OF
AGRICULTURAL DEVELOPMENT

THE ADMINISTRATION OF AGRICULTURAL DEVELOPMENT

LESSONS FROM INDIA

GUY HUNTER

With a Foreword by Anthony Tasker

LONDON
OXFORD UNIVERSITY PRESS
NEW YORK BOMBAY
1970

Oxford University Press, Ely House, London W.1

GLASGOW NEW YORK TORONTO MELBOURNE WELLINGTON
CAPE TOWN SALISBURY IBADAN NAIROBI DAR ES SALAAM LUSAKA ADDIS ABABA
BOMBAY CALCUTTA MADRAS KARACHI LAHORE DACCA
KUALA LUMPUR SINGAPORE HONG KONG TOKYO

SBN 19 215331 5

PRINTED IN GREAT BRITAIN BY
EBENEZER BAYLIS AND SON LIMITED
THE TRINITY PRESS, WORCESTER, AND LONDON

Foreword

THIS study was undertaken by Guy Hunter of the Overseas Development Institute, with the aid of a grant from the Rockefeller Foundation. It completes, by a detailed study of a particular region, a trio of books on the transfer of institutions, of which the first two—*The Best of Both Worlds?* and *Modernizing Peasant Societies*—were part of a project sponsored jointly by the Institute of Race Relations and the Overseas Development Institute and supported by the Ford Foundation.

In the practical task of development, which is the central concern of O.D.I., the administrator—say, the Director of Agriculture—is faced by problems which cannot be solved by purely technical decisions. He has to take into account social, economic, educational, administrative, and political factors which together make up the present stage of development of his country as a living and changing whole: in academic terms, his decision must be 'interdisciplinary'. In the earlier books Mr. Hunter emphasized the extreme selectivity which is needed in seeking to use, in developing countries, the technologies, the institutions, and indeed the type of economic and social thinking, which reflect the history and stage of development in highly industrialized countries. He went on to suggest, in very tentative terms, a description of the sequences of growth through which a developing country may pass, and the implications for practical policy which these stages may imply.

In this book the argument is brought down to a single, though very large, example—the current system for agricultural development in India—and is carried a step further. For policy has to consider not only the object of change—the rural society in its full dimensions—but the tools which can be expected to work effectively in changing it. At what stage can Cooperatives, or private enterprise, or a large bureaucratic Extension Service, be expected to succeed, not only in terms of their object but in terms of their own personnel, training, motives, political discipline?

We are still a long way from having a satisfactory framework of understanding which could give policy guidance on such questions. This book, although focused on India, suggests lines of thought which could have applications in many developing countries all over the world and could also influence the Aid policies of donors. In its future programme of studies in rural development, which will be greatly strengthened by close association with the University of Reading, O.D.I. hopes to contribute further in this field.

ANTHONY TASKER
Director, Overseas Development Institute

Contents

Acknowledgements

FIRST, I must acknowledge most gratefully the help of the Overseas Development Institute and of the Rockefeller Foundation, which respectively sponsored and financed this work. Dr. Soper of O.D.I. and Evelyn Wood in Bombay also most kindly read a first draft and made many valuable suggestions.

Second, both my wife and I owe a tremendous debt of gratitude to the Government of India, and especially to the States of Rajasthan, Uttar Pradesh, Bihar, Madhya Pradesh, and Maharashtra, and to the officers of the Agriculture Departments in each State who arranged our 1969 programme, accompanied us on extensive tours, and gave their time to answer a flood of questions, so that we might learn a little of all that they knew already. Alas, there is little that we can do to repay so much kindness and hospitality. There are a few suggestions in this book, and a sketch of a way of approach which might be of interest to them; but the main return, such as it is, may be to feel that the thought and effort which India has devoted to the administration of rural development may benefit not only India but many other countries, both in Asia and far beyond, where the Indian experiments are less well known than they should be.

Finally, this is in every sense a joint work. My wife travelled and worked with me on all our journeys, took the volumes of notes on which the book is based, made many valuable additions to the drafts, and typed the whole book for the press.

GUY HUNTER
Overseas Development Institute
August, 1969

Introduction

OVER the last few years many developing countries have given increasing attention and priority to agricultural development. It is not only because in most of these countries from 60% to 90% of population is found in the rural sector; high rates of population growth, low rates of absorption of the labour force into industry, and the consequent growth of unemployment have made it essential to generate more employment and more purchasing power in the rural economy.

Agricultural development has long been recognized as a difficult task. One of its chief tools, an Agricultural Extension Service, which is used by almost every country, has in many ways proved disappointing. Much has been written on the personnel and training needed for Extension, and on the methods of effective contact with farmers; it is not proposed to duplicate this here. There are, however, other factors which bear directly on the working effectiveness of an Extension effort, and it is on these that this study will concentrate.

There are four main subjects in this book. First, it concerns the coordination of administrative action by the government of a developing country in the provision of a complex service of information, technical help, investment, supply, credit, and marketing to peasant agriculture.

Second, it concerns the changing pattern of relationships between services directly supplied by government and those which the private commercial sector and Cooperatives of farmers can supply. These two subjects cover most of the straightforward comment on Extension as such.

Third, it concerns the relation between administrative action and the effort which many governments are anxious to make to draw the rural community into participation in the development effort, perhaps to give responsibility for some part of it to elected local committees; perhaps also to see that there is a political as well as an administrative channel through which local needs can be expressed.

These three problems are quite simply stated. But the fourth, which is both the most important and, I think, the most neglected, is more complex in itself and also deeply affects the first three. It is the double question of what type of effort can best be applied to a farming community at each of its changing stages of development, and, simultaneously, what type of organization, administrative, political, or private, can the developing society itself, in its own changing stages of growth, hope to apply effectively. Thus both the object and the tool are changing through time; and, further, both are intimately linked as parts of the same whole.

It is perhaps fairly widely recognized now, though not yet widely practised, that a different development and Extension approach is needed to farmers who are still largely in the grip of a traditional subsistence agriculture and a traditional cultural pattern from that which will work for farmers in active transition to a more commercial and individualist system, or, again, for farmers who have become both commercially minded and technically sophisticated. It is easy to suppose that, having made a correct diagnosis of the farmers' situation and attitudes, it is simply a matter of choosing the correct administrative tool. But this neglects the fact that society itself has not a total armoury of tools to choose from. In some stages of a developing society, to call for a large, efficient, honest, and well-coordinated bureaucracy is to ask for the moon; in some, to allocate a major function to private enterprise or Cooperatives may be equally futile; in some, to expect anything but self-interest and faction from local party-political activity may be to court disaster.

In the two earlier books of this trio[1] I tried first to point out the great danger, in such situations, of unselective borrowing by developing countries from the tools—institutions, administrative methods, technology—of highly developed and industrialized countries; unfortunately, this borrowing is often actively encouraged by expert advisers from those countries.

[1] *The Best of Both Worlds?* (O.U.P., London, 1967) and *Modernizing Peasant Societies* (O.U.P., London, 1969).

Of the many reasons for this caution, the most obvious is that these systems were evolved not only for different needs of a different type of farming community but also from the different capacities of developed societies, from resources (communications, literacy, skills, commercial enterprise, political experience, sheer wealth) which are not available to most developing countries.

The second book was more concerned to establish and trace the interconnections between various aspects of a growing society—economics, politics, administration, education, values —all of which, interacting, help to decree what kinds of task it can tackle and what kinds of tool it can command.

Both of those studies were necessarily put in fairly wide and general terms, applying to both Africa and Asia, although the second contained some considerable detail of the rural situation in India which is relevant to the present study. In the present book the object is to take as the focus a single concrete example of the operation of agricultural development effort, and particularly of an Extension Service, to see how the generalizations can be transformed into more or less detailed policy suggestions, and to trace how this fourth problem (of stages) works back upon the first three (coordination, private enterprise and Co-operatives, and democratic action).

2

To do this clearly involved choosing one country for study, although there are implications for many others and some passing references to them. There are great advantages in choosing India. It provides a large scale, and a tremendous range of conditions: there can be few types of agriculture not represented somewhere in India between the spices and coconuts and paddy-fields of Kerala and the wheat-fields and apple orchards below the Himalayas, between the dry, sparsely populated pastures of Rajasthan and the teeming settlements of Bengal. Secondly, India, in twenty years of independence, has made the most elaborate, self-conscious, and persistent effort to solve the problem of peasant agriculture which can be found anywhere in the developing world. Moreover, since agriculture is a subject mainly delegated to the eighteen Indian State Governments, there has been a chance of multiple experiments and variants on a single general policy, and this chance has been both used and evaluated in an extremely sophisticated way. These alternative models have invaluable lessons.

Certainly there are some implications from Indian experience which are not transferable to many other countries—for example, the quality of the top administration, or the amazing detail of the land-mapping, registration, and crop records. But India does offer an example of poverty—the annual *per caput* income is around £20—and of wealth; of modern industrialization carried very far, but alongside an old-established system of craft production; of a society already far along the road to development, yet still facing, among huge sections of her population, the very early stages of modernizing an ancient traditional form of rural life. In these respects she both shares the problems of much simpler developing societies and also exhibits the further stages of growth which, sooner or later, they too will face.

3

There is a further limitation to the scope of this study. To avoid going over too much well-trodden ground, I have not attempted to cover all the types of agricultural organization which can be used, but instead to concentrate very heavily on the problem which is both most widespread and most difficult. The sector which gives most trouble is not the plantation sector, which is usually organized as 'industrial agriculture' round processing factories; it is not the group of enterprising farmers with larger holdings and resources which are easily seen as economic for modern commercial production. It is the far larger sector consisting of a mass of small, often fragmented holdings, whether worked by owners or tenants or share-croppers, which characterizes up to half of the cultivated area and three-quarters of the farmers in most countries in Asia and tropical Africa.

The peculiar difficulty in developing this sector is that it seems to need a great deal of outside intervention. The farmers are often illiterate, often dominated by a 'subsistence' attitude to farming—they therefore need help from outside. They have difficulties with landlord systems or customary systems and with fragmentation—these difficulties can only be overcome from outside. The individual holdings at present provide too small and difficult a market for commercial suppliers of ferti-lizer or chemicals or tools—credit, supplies, and equipment have to be deliberately organized for them. Often ignorant of the movements of markets and prices, and powerless as indi-viduals to influence them, their efforts to increase production may be rewarded only by financial losses—again some organiza-tion and some regulation from outside is needed. It is these needs which have led to the creation of large official organiza-tions to educate and advise, to consolidate holdings, to supply inputs and services, to arrange credit, to organize marketing, and perhaps to control prices.

But while the importance of these needs has often been stressed, the many official reports and case-studies constantly underline the inadequacy of the resources devoted to meeting them—in terms of finance, personnel, transport, training—and the failures of coordination and effectiveness in the relevant administrative systems. There are indeed local and sometimes remarkable success stories. But in the wide sense we have not got an adequate understanding of the size and nature of the effort needed in various typical conditions, or, if the understanding is there at the technical level, the government is unwilling to grant the necessary resources. Nor is there any real agreement as to the best means of administrative direction and control. Indeed, there is a tendency to slide away from the difficulties in this sector and to emphasize how much quicker and more reward-ing it is to concentrate on the easier sectors—on industrial agriculture or private enterprise through the larger and better-educated farmers. To yield to this temptation is to forget that, in the present state of employment and population, only small-holding, labour-intensive agriculture can hope to provide a living for the inevitably increasing population of the rural sector.

The effort to deal with the small-holder sector has been going on for many years, and much money and effort has been put into it. It is irrational to continue to stress its importance and record its failures in the same breath, without a more vigorous attempt to assess what additional or different effort is needed to achieve a better return.

4

As to method, I have had to rely on description and the logical arguments derived from it. Strict cost-benefit analysis of the general effects of Extension is appallingly difficult. Even where a sharp rise in production or farm incomes appears to be linked to an Extension 'drive', it is impossible to identify single causes. A series of good seasons, a favourable price, the introduction of a new variety or technique, peculiar energy, intelligence, or education in the farming group affected, a pay-off from the long and apparently ineffective preceding effort in Extension work, the coming of a road, or the growth of a neighbouring town—all or any of these may have had critical significance. Obviously, a combination of necessary factors is involved; to weight the importance of any one of them is not merely difficult, it is irrational. It may be possible to separate the essential factors—without which nothing at all will happen— from the merely helpful factors, of which formal education may be one example. But if even three factors are indispensable— perhaps irrigation, a profitable market, and Extension—it is impossible to give relative weights to these three.

It may, however, be possible to make some useful progress by analysing single factors more closely. For example, in Extension education, there is a unit-cost per farmer/visit by Extension staff using bicycle transport; how many extra visits would be possible with a motor-bicycle, and with what effect on unit-costs? If the quality of the advice rather than the number of visits is critical, what would be the extra training and salary costs of providing better-trained personnel, and what proportion of the total agricultural budget would this represent? From rough figures in Chapter 9 it would appear that a 50% extra expenditure on field staff, whether in number or training or transport, might not mean more than an 8% or 9% increase in total agricultural recurrent expenditure and less than $\frac{1}{2}\%$ annual increase in total national expenditure if the increase is spread over 5 years; yet such an addition might be critical.

Such questions should certainly be asked, and answered. Perhaps they are not asked often enough by local governments— none of the five Indian and two African Agricultural Departments to whom these questions were put could answer them without some special enquiry. There is certainly room for careful local research. But such results, useful as they would be locally, would not support generalizations on 'ideal' strengths of personnel, or transport, or levels of training for the field service, all of which are essentially dependent on local conditions, the size of holding, literacy, road communications, and a host of other factors.

The book is arranged very simply in three sections. The first group of four short chapters deals mainly with structure and is almost wholly descriptive, to establish the facts and state problems. The second group (Chapters 6–8) deals with function and is mainly evaluative. The last chapter both summarizes and puts forward a number of suggestions and conclusions which seem to emerge from the logic of the study.

Finally, the field-work on which this study is based rests mainly on three journeys—to Delhi, the Punjab, Andhra Pradesh, and East and West Pakistan in 1967; to Orissa, Andhra Pradesh, Madras, Kerala, and Mysore in 1968; and to Rajasthan, Uttar Pradesh, Bihar, Madhya Pradesh, and Maharashtra in 1969. Gujarat, Haryana, Kashmir, Himachal Pradesh, Assam, and West Bengal are the omissions among Indian States, and we had only a very fleeting visit to the Punjab. In each case my wife and I spent the bulk of our time at the level of the Blocks and villages, and with the State administration. Almost all the references will therefore be to official documents, some of them published but many being the typed summaries of organization and performance which are so usefully provided at Block level. But the bulk of the information comes from many months of talking in Block offices, Village Panchayat centres, and on the farmers' fields. Once again, we would like to thank all our informants and helpers, including the State Governments, Panchayati Raj Departments, and universities in Orissa and South India who looked after us in 1968, and the scores of villages who offered us their unfailing hospitality.

PART 1

ORGANIZATION

CHAPTER 2

The Indian Background

INDIA has a total geographical area of just over 800 million acres, of which almost half is cultivable (381 million acres); the net sown area is 336 million acres.[1] The area is divided into some 50 million operational holdings, of an average size of $6\frac{1}{2}$ acres. Significantly for our purpose, 61·7% of the holdings are below 4 acres, and represent only 19·2% of the area, and a further 12·8% hold between 4 and $7\frac{1}{2}$ acres, representing a further 10·7% of the area. Thus three-quarters (74·5%) of the holdings are below $7\frac{1}{2}$ acres, and cover just under one-third (30%) of the cultivated area. Though statistical evidence is not conclusive, it is believed that farm size in India is decreasing—as might be expected from population growth. If this is true, it adds even greater urgency to the problem of servicing very small cultivators.

Total population is estimated at 511 millions (1967), growing by 12 millions per annum, with an annual *per caput* income of around £20. Of this total, roughly 80% live in the rural area, and 70% of the economically active population are agricultural (1965). It is of some interest that the working population in agriculture was divided in 1961[2] into roughly 100 million cultivators and 31 million labourers (these totals must now be increased), giving a proportion of 2 cultivators to each of the 50 million holdings.

2

Some very broad indications of the way in which land is held must be given, with the *caveat* that in actual practice there

[1] Statistics for 1965/6, from *Indian Agriculture in Brief*, 9th edn. (Ministry of Food, Agriculture, Community Development and Cooperation, Delhi, 1968).
[2] 1961 Census.

is a tangle of exceedingly detailed complexities and variations. For example, in those States where tenancy is legally prohibited, all sorts of arrangements, mostly in the form of share-cropping, in fact exist. Official statistics do not help in this, since the formal registration will always seem to be within the law, whatever its real nature.

Three major changes have taken place since Independence—the abolition of the *zamindari* system (see below), with reform of tenancy laws in many States; land reform; and a considerable effort towards land consolidation. Each of these is worth a word of comment.

It is usual to distinguish two different systems under which the Indian farmer worked at the time of Independence—the zamindari system, in which a *zamindar*[1] paid a fixed land revenue to government and collected from farmers within 'his' tract of land and villages; and the *ryotwari*[2] system, in which revenue was collected by government direct from the farmer. On the surface, this appears to be a distinction purely concerned with revenue collection. But over time the zamindari system, an adaptation by the British of the Moghul system which preceded it, had collected around it a multiplicity of payments, obligations, services, and dependencies from the cultivator to the zamindar and some countervailing obligations of protection, investment, and paternalism from the zamindar to 'his' cultivators. Zamindars in practice had overwhelming power in 'their' villages, and also provided a shield between the cultivator and the outside world. Some misunderstanding by the British of the old Moghul system, and considerable confusion as to the status of the zamindar—an indescribable mixture of feudal lord, landowner, and tax-farmer—had resulted in a system which was unique and which certainly had profound effects on agricultural life. In consequence, when zamindari was abolished after Independence, a certain vacuum was created which had to be filled administratively by government. For since the rights of zamindars were abolished so were their obligations. In those

[1] It is not necessary to describe at length what a zamindar was; and it is impossible to describe it accurately in a sentence. Very roughly, he was a person with whom the British administration made a settlement to deliver a fixed amount of land revenue from a fixed area of land. But the description in the text—'a mixture of feudal lord, landowner, and tax-farmer'—is more informative.

[2] *Ryot*=farmer.

States where zamindari had flourished, the cultivators suddenly found themselves in a ryotwari situation, as far as revenue collection was concerned, and also in a far more lonely and naked situation in so far as the previous protection and paternalism (as well as the exactions) of the zamindars had vanished. The zamindars themselves retained a nucleus estate of their old realm and became simply landowners.

But for our purpose these broad historical distinctions are less important than the underlying systems of tenure and payments which existed in various forms in both zamindari and ryotwari States, and much of which still exist today. For those of the villagers who worked land might hold it as traditional holders within the village community, with power to leave it to their children and power to sublet it to tenants or share-croppers; or they might hold it as fairly secure tenants to a real landlord—not necessarily a zamindar; or they themselves might be share-croppers, under a multitude of different arrangements as to rights and payments,[1] almost always bedevilled by uncertainty of tenure. Most States have enacted landlord-and-tenant legislation designed to outlaw some of the more undesirable features of these customary arrangements; but in practice, in disguised or undisguised forms, both share-cropping and tenancy remain widespread and important social factors right through the Indian agricultural scene. The Ford Foundation report on land tenure in Thanjavur District (Madras State[2]—an old ryotwari area) regarded the landlord system there as one of the major obstacles to the rapid spread of new farming technology among the cultivating tenants.

Thus the effect of one major change—the abolition of the zamindari system—has produced certain additional problems for the administrator, in providing a substitute for zamindar services; but the problem of providing advice,[3] inputs, and services to small cultivators as such, in any part of India, remains unchanged. It is, in fact, the landlord system rather than the revenue collection system which matters most.

---

[1] Most commonly, the cultivator provided bullocks and labour and received 50% of the main crop.

[2] I have retained the old name of Madras, as more familiar to English readers. Tamil Nadu is the correct modern name of the State.

[3] And of getting advice accepted when it comes from a government source.

The second major change after Independence was land reform, effected by means of a limitation on the size of individual holdings: in many States 30 acres of irrigated land is now the legal limit; in Uttar Pradesh it is as low as $12\frac{1}{2}$ acres. Although these limits are widely avoided (e.g., by registering 300 acres in ten 30-acre parcels in different family names), some millions of acres of land were surrendered, and small holders were moved into them, or the existing cultivators became holders from government. Here again, the government has had to supply the external assistance once provided, though at a cost, by the landlord.

The third change lies in the effort to organize land consolidation. In large areas of Uttar Pradesh this has been pushed forward successfully, and by the end of the Third Plan 15 million acres had been covered.[1] But in the bulk of India fragmentation is still the rule.

Thus the observer studying small-holder farming in India (holdings from, say, 2 to 10 acres) will find a mixture of conditions. The majority will be owners or owners holding from government; some of these will also be renting additional land from neighbouring farmers. But a large number will be tenants or share-croppers in various forms, both legal and illegal. In most cases their land will be in several fragments. Some, who hold only a few acres of dry land, may spend only a few weeks in the year on their own land (at sowing and harvest), and the rest of their time working as labourers or share-croppers for a bigger farmer who has water. Among the great mass of poorer families with small holdings it will be essential for at least some members of the family to work for wages for part of the year, to produce some handcraft goods for sale, or to provide some service rewarded in cash or kind.[2] At least 70% of the village adults will be semi-literate or illiterate. Agricultural wages will range (1969) from Rs. 2 (about 2/2½d)[3] to Rs. 4 (4/5d) per day—the high figure at harvest time when labour is short; but there are still some areas where the wage may be as low as

---

[1] Total cultivable area 45 million acres, of which the target for consolidation measures is only 30 million acres.
[2] Gilbert Etienne gives some excellent case-studies of the family budgets of Indian farmers in U.P., Madras, and Maharashtra. See his *Studies in Indian Agriculture* (University of California Press, Los Angeles, 1968).
Rs. 1=1/1⅜d; Rs. 7.5=1 U.S. dollar; Rs. 100=£5 11s. 1d.

Rs.1 per day. Net earnings from the land will be as low as Rs.150[1]
per acre per year in unimproved rainfed agriculture, rising to
Rs.1,000 for irrigated, high-yielding food grains, and even much
higher figures for horticultural or specialized crops under intensive cultivation—'lady's fingers' (*okra*) can yield Rs.3,000–
4,000 per acre gross, and grapes as much as Rs.15,000. Family
size per holding is likely to be between six and seven. Population
density naturally varies enormously. But on arable land some
idea of the scale could perhaps be given by indicating a range
of from 350 per square mile in 'low' density areas to a 1,200
average for Bengal or Kerala, and up to 2,000 in the patches of
highest concentration. At 1,000 per square mile the average
size of holding is likely to be around 2 acres.

It is impossible to give a picture of the 'typical' small holder
without specifying whether his land is only rainfed, or helped
by a domestic well, or by a tank, or by a tube-well, or by canal
irrigation; whether he is owner or tenant or share-cropper;
whether the local mean holding is 3 acres or 6 or 15 (15 is not
large in the Punjab, but it is quite a rich man's acreage in
irrigated delta areas of high density where two, three, or even
four crops may be grown in the year). But there are certainly
vast areas of India—including much of the Gangetic Plain
(U.P., Bihar, West Bengal) and the better-watered areas of
central and south India where the majority of the farmers would
be found among men working from 2 to 10 acres, of which 2 or
3 might be rented, on a fragmented holding, with perhaps a
quarter covered by some form of irrigation, with an average
net yield from traditional varieties of perhaps Rs.300–450 per
acre, taking the wet with the dry; and this man would be one
of the better farmers. Below him would be many with smaller
holdings, and all the landless labourers; above him would be a
few bigger farmers and landlords, of whom a growing number
will have adopted the new varieties and practices and are (at
present) making rich profits from their land.

Excluded from this picture are the dry pastoral areas of
India—for example, the dry parts of Rajasthan; very large
areas of purely rainfed agriculture in the Deccan Plateau and
elsewhere, where crops are poorer, holdings larger, incomes
lower; and areas, such as the tea areas of Assam, or the high

[1] Rs. 150=£8 6s. 8d, or just under 20 U.S. dollars.

rainfall areas of Kerala where coconut, spices, etc., produce a specialized pattern.

I have not attempted to sketch in the social background of rural life, including the problem of caste, partly because this was dealt with, however briefly, in *Modernizing Peasant Societies*,[1] partly because caste is a problem largely peculiar to India and Pakistan,[2] but above all because caste is a common factor of rigidity running through all productive, social, and administrative relationships and it is extremely improbable that the conclusions of this book would be any different if caste had been specifically taken into account. Caste can be taken as one element in the hierarchical structure of Indian society, alongside differences in wealth, education, political influence, etc., which makes effective help to the humbler members of society more difficult and which puts some grit into administrative relationships; as such it is certainly relevant to the tendency for the bigger and more powerful farmers to benefit most from the development effort.

3

The first great effort to tackle the uplift of the Indian rural masses in the early years of independence was based on a community development philosophy of broad-front attack on every aspect of village poverty—education, health, physical environment (roads, wells, etc.), agriculture, cottage industry, Cooperatives, women's work, emancipation of the Harijans (the 'untouchables'), land reform. The Community Development Department was given a great new responsibility. The whole of India was to be divided up into development 'Blocks', each of from 60,000 to 100,000 population, and two new cadres of Community Development workers were created—the Block Development Officers, and the Village Level Workers (*gramsewaks*). This Block system was to be made into a coordinating mechanism through which a total attack on village poverty could be mounted.

[1] O.U.P., 1969; especially Chapter II, 'Background and Change in Traditional Economies', and Chapter III, 'Status, Power, and Politics at Village Level'.
[2] Caste does not exist officially in Muslim Pakistan, but remains *de facto* of great importance.

There were four major points of emphasis in this strategy. First, on the Village Level Worker (V.L.W.), a high-school graduate with two years of training, paid about Rs.150–200 per month,[1] living in the village at not much above village standards, the helper and adviser, the single agent of all departmental programmes which directly touched village life. Second, an emphasis on the administrative Block, where rather more expertise would be concentrated in the shape of Extension Officers of agriculture, health, education, Cooperatives, water or road engineering, industries—all coordinated by a new figure, the Block Development Officer (B.D.O.), to whom all services were made operationally responsible. This officer was on the strength of the Community Development or Panchayati Raj Department, though seconded from some other existing service; he occupies a key place in the whole system. Third, there was the higher and more powerful point of authority and coordination at District level (1–2 million population), under the immense prestige of the Collector (District Magistrate or Deputy Commissioner),[2] the head of the District and leader of the District administrative team. Fourth, and in a different dimension, there was even greater emphasis on the creation of a system of popular elective participation by reorganizing, or shaping into a common form, the Village *Panchayat*[3] or council; and by creating entirely new Block and District level councils in parallel to the administrative Blocks and Districts. The panchayat system, at three levels, was to concern itself very directly with development. By a colossal demonstration of administrative energy, virtually the whole of India's population was brought within this network of over 5,000 Blocks and 250,000 Village Panchayats in less than ten years.

In the recollection of at least some administrative officers, this first period of 'Panchayati Raj'[4] and Block development was exciting, and in some senses productive, though many others groaned under the muddles and waste of energy which often accompanied it. The Blocks were given funds, and they

[1] About the same as the village Primary teacher.
[2] All three terms are used, in different States. D.C. will be used here as an abbreviation.
[3] In various forms, the village panchayat was a traditional organization in India, and the means by which a multitude of village affairs were regulated.
[4] Literally, 'Rule of the Panchayats'.

used them to build schools, village halls, paved village streets, and protected wells, all over India. The Village Level Workers were the agents of six or eight Departments, and they ran from the school garden to the voluntary road-gang, from the building of a covered bus-stop to the new compost pit, helping, reporting difficulties, and summoning aid.

But when the most glaring needs had been met, and when the early enthusiasm for voluntary effort began to run out of breath, reports started to come in from all over India that the basic problem of village poverty was not being solved. Indeed, much useful improvement of the village environment had been achieved—though roads need maintenance and compost pits must continue to be filled. Perhaps best of all, a new image of government as a source of help had been partially created. But the *production* of wealth—and basically this means the production from the land—had not been greatly affected. The villages, partly by their own efforts, had cleaned themselves up a little, they had some new buildings, and (perhaps most important) they had a stronger means of self-expression through the panchayats and a nearer source of help in the V.L.W.s and Blocks. But the scanty crops, the diet of rice or chapattis and a few green leaves, the indebtedness to moneylenders, continued as before. In 1958/9, after the powerful Balvantrai Mehta Report,[1] the emphasis was switched to production; 80% of the V.L.W.'s time was to be devoted to developing agriculture. The Ford Foundation's Intensive Agricultural District Programme was about to be launched; within another three years the new Philippine rice and Mexican wheat varieties, followed by huge improvements in maize, sorghum, and millets, were to come into use. Perhaps from 1963/4 onwards the new production programme began to gather impetus. It was held up in the drought years of 1966 and 1967, but sprang forward to the record harvests of 1968.

Today, the overwhelming emphasis of the whole programme is on production—though among a narrow sector of the 'progressive' (i.e., mainly the larger, better-educated, and more influential) farmers in irrigated areas. But in terms of organization the period of Community Development and Panchayati

---

[1] *Report of the Team for the Study of Community Projects and National Extension Service*, 3 vols. (Planning Commission, Delhi, 1957).

Raj has left a continuing mark. The multi-purpose nature of the Blocks continues; the Block Development Officer is still normally an employee of the Community Development or Panchayati Raj Department, not of the Department of Agriculture; the Collector and the whole range of Departments at District level are still involved; and, in some States particularly, the panchayats at Block level (at District level in Maharashtra) have become powerful local government bodies with a wide range of functions. It is in the light of this historical background that we can turn to look in detail at the present structure, and at the problems of coordination which it has raised.

CHAPTER 3

Administrative Coordination

I. THE NEED AND THE CONCEPT

THE need for coordination even in a purely agricultural programme—let alone a total rural development programme—seems clear enough. The small-holder section in particular will need advice (backed by research) in crop and animal husbandry; a veterinary service; improved tools and equipment. It will need help with wells and pumps for minor irrigation, and the pumps will need electricity supply. It will need credit, and before it is credit-worthy in commercial eyes. It will need an efficient distribution of seeds, fertilizer, and pest-control chemicals. It will need all this advice and service in a 'package', i.e., at the right time, in the necessary sequence, and without internal conflict in advice or services among the responsible agencies.

If, added to all this, the 'rural development' elements—education, health, village industries, clubs for women and young people, etc.—are thrown in as well, the task of coordination of agencies becomes formidable indeed. We have already mentioned subjects covered by more than half the Departments which a State Government is likely to have—Agriculture, Veterinary, Water, Engineering, Communications, Power, Community Development, Health, Education, Social Services, Finance, and District Administration. It is clear that these cannot be rolled up into one super Ministry; it is clear that the point of unified advice and service must be the point which is as near as is practical to the farmer himself. But the all-purpose Village Level Worker cannot function if he gets conflicting instructions from the Block, nor the Block if there is confusion at District, nor the District if there is confusion in the State.

This is the traditional justification for the demand for more or better administrative coordination. But before looking at the actual problems which it poses, it is worthwhile to consider for a moment one or two implications of the concept itself.

In the first place, coordination implies an antithesis to consumer choice. If there are plenty of goods and services on the market in wide variety, the consumer does all the necessary coordination by the process of selection and timing to suit his own purposes and his purse. Conflicting advice and competing tools and materials are available in plenty to farmers in developed countries. To make consumer choice work there must be plenty—not shortages—on the supply side and a certain level of competence, business sense, willingness to take technical advice, and independence or resources on the consumer side. The economist's emphasis on 'scarce resources' in supply, and the ignorance, poverty, or dependence of the consumer are at the roots of planning, State socialism, and 'coordination'.

Secondly, as the literature on industrial management has so often pointed out, coordination has a hostile ring to its victims, since it implies a loss of sovereignty; if the works chemist is to be coordinated with the works engineer by the works manager, both feel that they are losing an element of sovereignty (and in their own special field) and each suspects others of imperialism. Nowhere is this suspicion stronger than among Ministers and government departments. The problem is worse where power is highly centralized and detail is decided at the top—the process of carrying this detail down a long hierarchy of command maximizes the possibilities of dispute and suspicion as well as the probability that local variations in need will be ignored. As long as administration is thought of as a power system rather than a technical collaborative system, coordination will cause trouble.

Trouble is particularly certain in developing countries, which are especially characterized by shortage of resources—'shortage' is of course related to the ambitions of achievement; more modest ambitions automatically reduce it. They are also characterized by centralization of power. Finally, they are characterized by the ignorance and poverty of the consumer. It is because central government, in an agricultural development programme, is endeavouring to do a great number of specific things to (or for) a mass of small producers who are assumed to be unable to do them autonomously, that co-ordination causes such constant anxiety and friction. The farmer is even given bags of fertilizer rather than the credit to use at his discretion. It is significant that the richer and more powerful farmers do not create such a problem of coordination; they make their own choice of what is available and buy it when they need it.

These very simple propositions do, of course, suggest the main antidotes to the disease of coordination. A certain prudence in ambitions will at once reduce the fever. Maximum decentralization of detailed decision will narrow the area where it rages. A philosophy of enablement rather than provision or enforcement will simplify the task. In effect, the administrative problems of rural development should constantly decrease as the process succeeds. Good information to a farmer capable of understanding it, and at least a minimum range of choice to suit his needs, are the ultimate targets; it is vitally important in the whole discussion which follows that these objectives should not be lost to sight.

There is, finally, the question of timing. The American belief that a good university pouring out Extension information, and a private sector for supplies, are the right medicine for developing countries is wrong in present action simply because it is premature. If the problem is to uplift a mass of farming units which, in their present state, are not economically viable, through illiterate farmers who are indebted and socially or politically dependent, then a great deal has to be done executively and supplied artificially before the free economy can take over. It is this task which faces developing countries at this present moment; and it is the temptation to shirk it and uplift only those who can respond, thanks to their education and their financial and political power, which is giving rise to the philosophy of 'backing the winners' whatever the future social costs may be.

Some modesty in targets; an attempt to design coordinating machinery as technical collaboration rather than administrative sovereignty; maximum delegation of detail; enablement rather than provision or enforcement; and a timing of these policies suited to real conditions—these are the main guidelines in considering the coordinating policies which have been devised and followed in the remarkable experiments which India has been making.

2. THE ACTUAL STRUCTURE AND ITS VARIANTS

Figure 1 (p. 32) shows in schematic form the main lines of the Indian chain of command from State level to the farmer. It is designed to achieve three main objects. First, a single point of contact at the village—the V.L.W. Second, a nucleus of better-trained personnel, finance, and direction at the Block, under the operational control of a single officer—the B.D.O. Third, a more powerful centre of authority and coordination at the District, symbolized in the prestige of the Collector. It was not specifically designed to cover coordination at the highest level—the State.

(a) *Block Level.* The functions of the Block and of the Block Development Officer are fairly uniform throughout the Indian States—to establish these Blocks was the cardinal stroke of policy in 1952. The technical staff at this level cover the agricultural, animal husbandry, veterinary, fishery, crop-protection, soil conservation, and minor irrigation functions; credit, usually through a Cooperative officer; women's work; education; information and statistics; sometimes industry. It was clearly felt that this quite large team[1] needed leadership, and (more dangerously) direction; and that the leader must therefore be given definite operational control. This last decision is one which most governments in other developing countries have feared to take, since it cuts the chain of command of several Departments. How far it contravenes the guide-line which suggests technical collaboration rather than administrative sovereignty depends to some extent on the training of the B.D.O. and on his own view of his job; but it goes far in that direction by giving him actual authority rather than forcing him to achieve collaboration without it. It could well be defended on 'timing' grounds—that in a new situation, at the present level of training, and in the still live background of an authoritarian tradition, only authority would be respected. We shall come back to this point.

[1] In some States two functions at least are carried by a single officer.

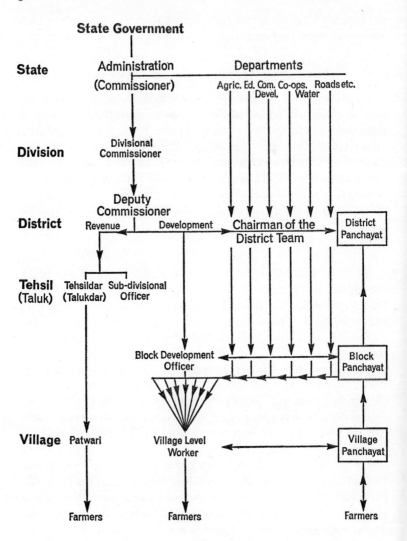

FIG. I

Two more guide-lines—modesty in target-setting and delega-tion of detail—have certainly been neglected at Block level: the whole system revolves round detailed targets set from above and is bedevilled by shortages; but this relates to content and functioning and belongs to Part 2.

One State—Madhya Pradesh—has abolished the B.D.O. It was argued that the full team of Extension officers was not needed in many Blocks and that the B.D.O., with so many services at his local command, could too easily be captured by politicians to serve their interests. These are interesting reasons, which have some significance in future argument. A little surprisingly, the decision was regretted by many field staff (including the Agricultural Extension staff), who missed the team spirit, the focus of achievement, and the sense of dedication which had been noticeable in the earlier period of Community Development emphasis.

It is worth noting the nature of the B.D.O.'s appointment. He is not a sub-divisional officer (D.O.I. in African termino-logy) on the Collector's (D.C.'s) staff. He is seconded from any of several Departments (Agriculture, Education, Customs, or Revenue itself), is officially on the strength of the Community Development or Panchayati Raj Department, but is operation-ally answerable to the Collector. He is supposed to get a three-month or six-month training for the post, and on leaving it will normally revert to his old parent Department, often with promotion. This arrangement probably springs from two causes. Historically, the Block organization was a Community Development effort; the Department had to borrow staff in its enormously rapid expansion. Secondly, there was probably a wish to avoid the 'Revenue mentality'—of which more later—by appointing an officer from another Department or, if from the Revenue Department, putting him on a different establish-ment. In Rajasthan an ex-Agricultural officer is normally appointed B.D.O. in an intensive cropping Block, an Animal Husbandry officer in a cattle Block, and a man with educa-tional or social training in Blocks where the production programme is small and Community Development the main activity.

It may be noted that in East Pakistan the 'Circle Officer', who is the Community Development Department official at

3

Thana (Block) level, does not have authority over the other officers at his level.

(b) *District Level.* The Collector or Deputy Commissioner is naturally head of the District team, and always has been in India. But he now has much more specific development responsibility, and has been given accordingly more formal authority over the Extension staff at District level and over the Blocks.

However, he has an immense work-load as District Magistrate, Revenue Collector, and Deputy Development Commissioner rolled into one. Various means of supporting him have been evolved. One method, and the most common, is to give him an additional officer on the Revenue side,[1] so that he can concentrate on development. He may also be given a Personal Assistant almost exclusively devoted to development work (e.g., in Madras). The alternative is to put in an 'Additional District Magistrate' or 'District Planning Officer' (U.P.—both terms are used), who concentrates wholly on development. Gilbert Etienne[2] noted that in U.P. this weakened the drive from District level—the A.D.M. or D.P.O. had not the quality and authority of the D.C. himself. In Rajasthan the title is Assistant Development Commissioner. There are several special variants. In Maharashtra the District-level panchayat (*Zila Parishad*) has been given full executive authority, funds, and staff. The District and Block staff are paid for and controlled by this Committee, and the 'Chief Executive Officer' at District level is an I.A.S.[3] man of Collector rank, who has probably held a Collector's post before. The Collector, alongside, concentrates wholly on Revenue and Magistrate work. The implications of this situation are considered below in relation to panchayat functions. In Bihar the Collector is given a 'Special Project Officer' who looks after most of the Block programme, but the Collector appears to retain a strong interest in development work—his own description was 60% on development, 30% law and order, 10% Revenue, for which he has a deputy.

In the Intensive Agricultural District Programme (I.A.D.P.)

[1] E.g., a District Revenue Officer is appointed in Andhra Pradesh.
[2] G. Etienne, op. cit.
[3] Indian Administrative Service.

Districts, which were started in some fifteen States, a Project Officer for the High-Yielding Varieties Programme is appointed, sometimes with the rank of Joint Director of Agriculture (Thanjavur), which is a step higher than that of the District Agricultural Officer (normally a Deputy Director). The Project Officer holds a position at District level roughly equivalent to that of B.D.O. at the Block as a coordinator; he will look to the Collector for general authority and guidance in the District, and to the Director of Agriculture on technical matters.

Apart from an additional post alongside the Collector, there is a tendency to use Revenue staff (e.g., a Revenue Divisional Officer) to supervise the Blocks and panchayats, particularly on the financial and auditing side (Madras,[1] Andhra Pradesh). While the supremacy of the Collector himself is accepted without question in the District, this use of Revenue officers inside the development structure, looking over the shoulder of the B.D.O., the panchayat chairman, and the Agricultural Extension staff, is apt to be resented.

One more radical innovation must be mentioned. In Andhra Pradesh the powers of the Directors of development Departments—including the Director of Agriculture and the Registrar of Cooperatives—have been delegated to Collectors, the Directors becoming technical advisers and a link with the Secretariat. This enables the D.C. to take any decision open to the Directors, including financial authorizations; and the D.C. with the chairman of the Zila Parishad form a two-man 'Development Board' with almost total powers over the whole development programme in the District.

On the whole, these variants mainly tend in one direction— to strengthen the District administration in some degree at the expense of the initiative and authority of the Block. Either the Collector is drawn more and more fully into the development field, while his Revenue functions are carried by an alternate,

---

[1] E.g., in Madras: 'The Collector is also assisted by the Revenue Divisional Officer, who combines in himself the supervisory functions both on the revenue and on the development side so far as the Division is concerned. All the revenue grants to the [Panchayat] Unions are being sanctioned by the R.D.O., on post-execution basis. . . . The R.D.O. also reviews the programmes and is primarily responsible for the execution of the Development Programmes throughout the Unions.' *Panchayat Development in Madras State* (Government of Madras, 1967).

or a special officer is appointed at District to energize, supervise, and direct the Blocks. Only in one State (Madhya Pradesh) has the chief technical Department (Agriculture) recovered full authority at Block level and maintained its position at District level. There are, however, signs that the Maharashtra Agricultural Department is moving in the same direction, by appointing, in areas of intensive agricultural development, additional *Agricultural* Assistants, alongside the V.L.W.s but directly responsible to the Agricultural staff above them, and with no community development responsibilities. The Maharashtra Agricultural Department has suggested that there should be a special Agricultural B.D.O. in the intensive areas.

Secondly, the Panchayati Raj or Community Development Department has been gently moved aside from the centre of the stage, which is held now by the District Administration, with the Agricultural Department in second place; this reflects the shift to a production and technical emphasis as against the earlier emphasis on social and environmental services.

Once again, the emphasis is on administrative sovereignty rather than on the technical departments. It would, I think, be defended in India by quoting the need for decisive and speedy resolution of constant interdepartmental overlaps or tensions, and by the need for a single line of control of the very considerable revenues flowing through the District. As the shortages are overcome, as farmers themselves become more autonomous, and as the technical element in the programmes becomes more sophisticated and essential, the Agricultural and Engineering Departments may well be able to break out of the grip of the B.D.O., and even assert themselves more strongly at the District level.

(c) *State Level*. Despite two levels of coordination below State level, it has been found necessary to modify the traditional structure even at the State Government level. The method chosen has been usually to create 'overlords' with a title emphasizing either Production or Development. Thus, while there may be both a Secretary and a Director for Agriculture, for Cooperatives (Registrar), for Community Development or Panchayati Raj, and for Engineering (Chief Engineer), there is in many States an overlord, called usually Secretary and

Development Commissioner, who is coordinating the development programme. Generally speaking, these overlord posts will deal with the Districts on development matters; but it must be remembered that each State also has a Chief Secretary, who will not only be Secretary to the Cabinet but also the head of the District Administration (Divisional Commissioners and District Collectors) at least in so far as they are carrying out their Revenue and Magistrate functions. An additional complication lies in the Planning function, which is bound to stretch across Departmental boundaries.

We did not investigate the problems of this level, which would form part of a study of public administration in central government rather than a study of Extension. But it is clearly of great importance to the functioning of lower echelons, and has puzzled many governments outside India. Pakistan, for example, has leaned towards creating special public corporations (the Agricultural Development Corporation, Water and Power Development Administration, etc.) with troublesome overlaps between the A.D.C. and the Ministry of Agriculture. Thailand has failed to secure coordination, leaving the Department of Agriculture, the Rice Department, the Royal Irrigation Department, the Ministry of the Interior, the Ministry of National Development, the National Economic Development Board, and even the Prime Minister's Office, to battle with problems of agricultural planning and development under their separate banners. Taiwan invented the Joint Rural Reconstruction Committee; Tanzania established a Settlement Board to handle a £13 million scheme for villagization and new settlement—the Board had to beg or borrow its Extension staff from the Ministry of Agriculture; Kenya, rather than create a new entity, has settled for a National Rural Development Committee of Permanent Secretaries, built round a nucleus of President's Office, Treasury, and Planning, and bringing in the 'operating' Ministries (Agriculture, Labour, Local Government, Social Services, Public Works, etc.) for their respective interests and programmes. Malaysia created perhaps the most powerful unit in a Ministry of Rural Development headed by the Deputy Prime Minister and supervising also the extremely powerful Federal Land Development Authority.

If the guide-lines throw any light on this issue, it is that a higher degree of delegation to the field might avoid the necessity of creating new super-Ministries or Boards, since the major policy decisions should be few enough to settle in normal Cabinet or special committee procedure—'entities should not be multiplied unnecessarily' is a good motto in government as well as in philosophy. Since central government must necessarily be divided into Departments, and since three-quarters of the Departments will be involved in rural development, there may not be much point in bunching a few—but not all—of the relevant ones under an overlord.

3.   THE CREDIT STRUCTURE

Apart from moneylending, and from some private commercial and bank credit normally obtainable only by the better-off and credit-worthy farmers, there are two main official channels through which credit is made available:

(1) *Taccavi Loans*. These are loans given through the Revenue Department, secured by a mortgage on land, usually for a short term of a year. The application usually has to be processed through the *Patwari*[1] and approved by the *Tehsildar*.[2] The Revenue Department is responsible for recovery. In some States (e.g. in Orissa), Taccavi is reserved mainly to meet emergencies (e.g., a crop failure, famine conditions, floods, etc.). In others (e.g. in U.P.), up to 40% of the short-term official credit to farmers may be through Taccavi.

(2) *Cooperative Loans*. Short-term crop-loans are most widely given through Primary Cooperative Societies and recovered from the Societies by the financing organization. The credit system stretches back through Cooperative Unions or District Societies to a State Apex Bank or Finance Corporation of some kind, and finally to the Reserve Bank of India. The amounts requested are originally based on estimates made by the V.L.W. of what acreage of crops requiring cash inputs will be grown by cultivators in each village; these are approved by the Primary Society and forwarded upwards. If the Society is in default (less

---

[1] Village Clerk and Revenue Agent.
[2] Revenue Officer at Tehsil level.

ADMINISTRATIVE COORDINATION

than 60% repayment is the usual criterion), no credit is given in the following year, even to individuals who are fully paid-up. The Primary Society, often aided by the V.L.W., must make its own recoveries from individuals. Loans are technically secured on the crop in most cases. The maximum loan is usually calculated as twenty times the assessed land revenue for the applicant's land, or ten times his deposit in the Cooperative.

Somewhat larger loans are also given on a medium-term (up to five years) or long-term (fifteen years or more) basis for capital improvements (chiefly wells and pumps; occasionally tractors, cattle-purchase, land levelling, buildings, poultry units, and grape-gardens, etc.). These loans are more usually given through a Land Mortgage Bank or Land Development Bank or Agricultural Finance Corporation. A formal mortgage is necessary, and the application forms (up to 40 pages of questions!) are long and complicated. The V.L.W.s and Block staff spend much time filling them up for cultivators and helping to get them through the stages of sanction.

The amount of short-term credit has gone up by leaps and bounds over the last decade; and the share of credit handled by the Cooperatives has also increased quite sharply. The Reserve Bank Rural Credit Surveys show a rise in the Cooperative share from 3% in the early 1950s to 10%/12% by 1960 and 19% by 1964. It is probably now over 25% for the whole country, and well over that in some States which have made a special drive to get out credit through the Cooperative organization. Nevertheless, it must be remembered that far the biggest sources of credit are still private—relations, friends, the moneylender, and the landlord.

4. MINOR IRRIGATION

There is almost always a division between 'major' irrigation, involving large dams and canals, and a wide variety of minor irrigation, which will include tube-wells and bore-wells, shallow dams (usually called 'tanks' in India), which may only hold water for a few months, minor works on hillside streams, again largely seasonal, lift-irrigation by pumps from rivers, Persian Wheels on wells, etc. In most States the Agricultural Department will look after minor irrigation, while the major works are retained by the Engineering Department. In some cases, Blocks have their own minor irrigation schemes, and in Madras State the Revenue Department has Food Production Circles with funds for minor irrigation works.

For reasons which are partly historical the engineers considered themselves superior to the agricultural staff; they did indeed have responsibilities for huge irrigation schemes at a time when agriculture was a far less technical subject.[1] Perhaps for this reason, coordination seems especially difficult between the two, and the evaluation reports are full of instances of independent action or failure to cooperate. The B.D.O. never obtained such direct operational control of the engineers as he has over the Agricultural and Community Development staff, again because engineering, like medicine, is regarded as an esoteric profession while agronomy is not. However, now that water is seen so clearly to be just as much an agricultural input as seed or fertilizer, for which timeliness and adequacy are as important, it is clear that far closer relations are needed and that minor irrigation is, or should be, an Extension specialism as much as animal husbandry. There are a great number of variants in the Indian States in this particular field of coordination, but at least it is under very active review. In contrast, in tropical Africa large irrigation, water for stock, and (increasingly) domestic water have occupied a good deal of attention, very often dealt with by an Engineering Department, an Animal Husbandry Department, and a Health or Community Development Department respectively, notably omitting the Agriculture Department; minor irrigation for intensive cropping and new varieties has been far less developed.

[1] Moreover, the engineers could levy a cess on villages for the works they managed—not always without a private profit—while the agricultural staff could not.

CHAPTER 4

The Elected Councils

THE essential function of the panchayat system in its traditional, village forms was to settle disputes by persuasion and to maintain the traditional caste and customary order of the village; as such it had some similarity with a council of elders in some African tribal systems. This old system, with its many variations in different parts of India, offered to the modern administrator a possible tool for securing the expression of popular needs and wishes and for involving 'the people' in the development process. As such, it was renovated (and thereby greatly changed), formalized, largely standardized, financed, extended to Block and District level, and fitted to the new administrative structure for rural development which was created in the 1950s.

Much closer analysis of what was in fact expected of this renovated and expanded system, and how it has worked in practice in both administration and politics, is given in Chapter 8; this chapter simply sets out the new structure and formal functions, with some discussion of the variations in methods of election and duties which exist and of the possible reasons for them.

As to electoral systems, there is not much variation at the level of the village (*grampanchayat*).[1] In most States the election of some 5–15 members is by secret ballot on adult suffrage, in some States by the village assembly (*Gram Sabha*), and in one or two by show of hands. The president is usually elected by the members, but in some States more directly by the village assembly. Unanimous election (which involves a lot of parleying and intrigue beforehand) is strongly favoured in the Hindu

[1] There are variations in the titles by linguistic regions: *Grampanchayat* for the village, *Panchayat Samiti* for the Block, and *Zila Parishad* for the District are perhaps the best known transliterations. 'President' is used here for the village chairman and 'chairman' for the Block chairman.

religious tradition and officially supported in some States,[1] and villages which achieve it may even be given a reward from public funds. There is provision, reflecting all-India policy, for reserving a seat for a woman member and also for representation of 'scheduled castes' (i.e., untouchables, now called *Harijans*) and 'scheduled tribes' (usually more backward communities).

At the Block level, variations are more important, though not very extensive. In the great majority of States the Block Panchayat is composed of the presidents of the Village Panchayats in the Block, with the usual reservation of seats, but with the addition of the Members of the State Legislative Assembly (M.L.A.s) and Legislative Council (M.L.C.s) and of the all-India Parliament (M.P.s); in most cases a member or members of the Cooperatives are added, and some representation of urban areas in the Block is also covered. There is, however, one State (Mysore) in which the Block Panchayat is directly elected on adult suffrage; in Assam, Madhya Pradesh, and Punjab the members are elected by a college of all members of Village Panchayats in the Block; and a similar, though slightly different, system is used in Maharashtra.

The District Councils (Zila Parishad) are normally composed, *ex officio*, of the chairmen of Block councils, sometimes with the addition of an extra member from each council elected by its members. There are the usual reservations and provision for adding Cooperative and urban members, M.L.A.s, etc., and, occasionally, specially qualified individuals. There is one outstanding exception—Maharashtra—where the Zila Parishad has 40–60 members directly elected from the District, in addition to the Block chairmen and the other reserved, *ex officio*, or coopted seats. There are certain compromises in Gujarat, where there is some direct election in addition to the Block chairmen, and in U.P. and Punjab, where a certain number of members, in addition to the chairmen, are elected by all primary members of the Block councils.

In almost all States provision is made for membership or

[1] An all-India sample of village respondents showed that no less than 55·9% of respondents preferred a unanimous election, against 21·5% for a contested election, and 22·6% 'don't know' or other answers: see Lalit K. Sen and Prodipto Roy, *Awareness of Community Development in Village India* (National Institute of Community Development, 1966).

attendance of the Block and District officials of development Departments, sometimes with a right to speak but not vote, sometimes for consultation only. In cases where either of the councils is not really a panchayat but a Block or District Development team, with some unofficials added, the B.D.O. or Deputy Commissioner respectively will be chairman and the officials full members. These shades of difference obviously reflect varying decisions at State level as to the degree of authority and influence which can be entrusted to the democratic body and the amount of power which the official hierarchy wishes to retain.[1]

These variants in electoral systems are extremely significant, since they provide evidence of the political judgement of each State as to the real role of elected institutions in local development. The arguments in favour of the indirect systems of election are that the village presidents are most directly in touch with the real needs and problems of farmers and citizens in the face-to-face situations and relationships of the village; that they are able to express these needs in concrete and even technical terms, not in the rhetoric and generalizations of party politics; that a Block council consisting of these village leaders will at least carry some of this grass-roots atmosphere and realism to a higher level; that even a District council consisting of these Block chairmen will carry the same directness, though in much diluted form. Moreover, since the directly elected M.L.A.s, M.L.C.s, and M.P.s are added to the Block and District councils, the element of directly elected party representation will be present in any case.

It is reasonable to deduce that those States which adopted indirect systems saw the panchayats mainly as a channel for *participation* by ordinary citizens, a means by which official policies, if they passed the test of popular approval, should have the help and even enthusiasm of the people behind them. There were even strong arguments against the cooption of M.L.A.s and M.P.s on the grounds that party politics should be kept at arm's length in these participatory bodies—indeed, party labels are not used in the panchayat elections.

[1] Full details of the electoral system and composition of panchayats as at 1966 were kindly provided by the National Institute of Community Development (Hyderabad, Andhra Pradesh). For a massive and comprehensive study of structure, function, and finances, see Sugan Chand Jain, *Community Development and Panchayati Raj in India* (Allied Publishers Private Ltd., Bombay, 1967).

The arguments for the direct systems are equally interesting. It was felt that the village presidents were likely to be the village magnates—landlords, merchants, caste-dominants, etc.—whom the villagers would not dare to oppose within the village and who might well represent their own interests rather than the common need. To carry them up to Block and District automatically would never let in a new element of leadership, elected directly in the more impersonal atmosphere of a Block (100,000 population) or a District election (1½ million). Further, it is argued that the attempt to exclude party politics is both irrational and doomed to failure. Political parties supposedly exist to express popular needs and ambitions; if they are corrupt, they will ultimately be reformed by new parties; and in any case they are totally pervasive—the labels may not be used but everyone knows who are the Congress candidates and who are not.

There is a fundamental argument of political philosophy, administrative policy, and timing underlying these decisions, which is of great interest to developing countries.

2

As to powers and responsibilities of the panchayats, there is again a range of variation. Some States are cautious, and especially about the Zila Parishad, which has been abolished in Orissa, which had not come into existence in Kerala (Spring 1968), and which is advisory or consultative in all States except four (U.P., Punjab, Maharashtra, and Gujarat, notably States with a more direct elective system). Some States, including Kerala, have a District Development Council, chaired by the D.C., which is really the District team of officials with some unofficials coopted to it. The Block councils are more heavily used as executive or semi-executive organs in most States, although several still describe them as purely consultative.

At the extreme of the bolder States stands Maharashtra, which has given to the Zila Parishad at District level a large budget,[1] wide-ranging executive powers over the field of local government and development, and a full staff. Under their

[1] In 1966, over Rs. 17 per head of population, representing one-third of total State recurrent expenditure.

Chief Executive Officer, of Collector rank, the whole District staff of the development Departments are deployed, roughly as in any English County Council, as the servants of the Zila Parishad. This will, of course, include the agricultural staff (the senior man is called the Agricultural Development Officer), whose relationship with the State Director of Agriculture and his joint Directors is in theory a purely technical advisory one. The Block Panchayat and Block staff are, broadly speaking, subsidiaries of the Zila Parishad.

Andhra Pradesh has also gone a long way to strengthen the executive function of the Block Panchayats (staff is being transferred to a separate local cadre), and to give the Zila Parishad wide responsibilities in planning and stimulating development, although it is advisory and consultative. The two-man District Development Board (chairman of the Zila Parishad, plus Collector with powers of departmental Directors) has very wide authority over the whole District development programme, excluding a few subjects, such as major irrigation, which go beyond the District boundaries and finances. The Block Development Officer in Andhra, as in most States where the Block has executive powers, is the chief executive for the Block Panchayat; how far the Panchayat really instructs him, and how far they take his advice and ask him to implement it, depends mainly on the strength and forcefulness of the Panchayat (particularly of its chairman) in local circumstances.

3

The system of financing the whole pyramid of panchayats is complicated, with many variants in different States. There is, to start with, one general provision by which Blocks were given a substantial grant in their first five years (Stage 1), a reduced amount in their second five years (Stage 2), and nothing thereafter (Stage 3) when they would be considered mature and able to manage with their other sources of revenue.

These other sources can be divided into two groups—revenue raised by the panchayat itself within its own constituency, and revenue coming from 'above'. The latter takes many different forms—matching grants, to match revenue locally raised; shares of certain taxes, and commission for collecting them; funds channelled through the panchayats for particular Departmental functions, such as funds for Primary schools via the Education Department; whole or matching grants for particular campaigns (for example, the Rural Manpower programme, designed to give employment in off-seasons on public works projects); funds delegated to village councils by the Block, or to Blocks by the District.

There is a very wide range, not only between States, but between all levels within a State, of the actual amounts of cash which the various levels may handle, partly depending on the energy of the local council in raising its own revenue, partly on whether a Block is in Stage 1, 2, or 3 (the starting dates differed), partly on State policy. The councils with executive or semi-executive powers, particularly where these include older local government functions in health, education, etc., naturally have the largest budgets. What is universal is that self-raised revenue seldom rises above 10%–20% of total revenue; the panchayats are largely 'kept' by the State and Union Governments.

To give some idea of scale, total revenue at the village level will *average* nationally between Rs.2 and Rs.1 per head; but this average conceals a range between States of from Rs. 4 or 5 per head (and even higher) to less than Rs.0·5. This range may be from Rs.9 to Rs.1 within a single State.[1] However, an 'ordinary' Village Panchayat in an 'ordinary' State may have Rs.4,000 to Rs.6,000 to spend for its 2,000–3,000 population.[2]

At Block level the variation is also very great. In 1961/2 the

[1] These financial figures are mainly extracted from Dr. Sugan Chand Jain's study, op. cit.

[2] For example, here are population and revenue figures for four Village Panchayats visited in Oddanchatram Block, Madurai District, Madras State:

		Population	Revenue
1.	Kalanjipatti	1,350	c.Rs.2,000
2.	Muthanaickenpatti	4,230	c.Rs.6,000
3.	Idayacottai	3,476	c.Rs.6,000
4.	Chattrapatti	2,776	c.Rs.4,500

At a higher level, Village Panchayat incomes in Hayatnagar Block, Andhra Pradesh, were distributed as follows: 10 at Rs.10,000 and above; 15 at Rs.5,000–10,000; 16 at Rs.2,000–Rs.5,000. The *average* population of a panchayat in this Block is about 2,500. In Bhor Block, Poona District (Maharashtra), average village revenue per head was Rs.3·75.

higher figures for Madras, Andhra Pradesh, Orissa, and Rajasthan were Rs.11, Rs.10·94, Rs.8·53, and Rs.6 per head respectively. Lower figures for Maharashtra and U.P. were Rs.4·86 and Rs.2·19 respectively. Figures for District (Zila Parishad) incomes are much of the same range but rising in some Maharashtra Districts to over Rs.18 per head; they are least of all comparable because the powers and responsibilities of the Zila Parishad are so different in different States. Appendix I shows the Revenue sources for Panchayats and Panchayat Unions (Blocks) in Madras State.

4

In broad terms, India is thus more than halfway along the road to a full three-tier local government system within the States. The Village Panchayats already fill the bill at their level. The Block Panchayats, where they are executive, cover the development subjects, and they are very wide when Health and Education are included as part of Community Development. A list of subjects handled in an Andhra Pradesh Block[1] (see pp. 49–50)—and many Blocks in other States could provide similar examples—shows how wide their responsibility is, and the large element of Community Development which they carry.

How far is this participatory or political activity helpful to agricultural development? At what stage of political, economic, and educational sophistication is it reasonably likely to work well? How far is it necessary in any case, or could a paternal and efficient administration produce results both more quickly and to public satisfaction? Is it possible to keep a participatory organization separate from a formal local government system?[2] Should staff be transferred to the local council or remain on the central government payroll? Is the supervision and veto of a D.C. needed, and in what circumstances and for how long? How far can agricultural policy and execution follow a logical line and extend to all classes of farmers, if it is to any extent controlled by elected bodies on which political, merchant, and large-farmer interests predominate?

[1] Medchal Panchayat Samiti, near Hyderabad.
[2] Perhaps the clearest distinction can be seen outside India—for example, in the 'Self-help' committees of Kenya, which are quite separate from County Councils.

These are some of the questions which are raised by the mixed structure of official administration and elected councils in India and for which some answers must be attempted later in this book.

MAIN FUNCTIONS OF MEDCHAL PANCHAYAT SAMITI, 1968

(Andhra Pradesh)

Population (1961) 92,555. 101 villages, 43 grampanchayats, 10 V.L.W.s. Annual Budget Rs.1,500,000.

I. *Agriculture*

Distribution of Improved Seeds
Supply of Fertilizers and Pesticides
Distribution of Improved Implements
Japanese Method of Paddy Cultivation
Loan Schemes—wells, cattle purchase, crop loans, electric motors for pumps
Rural Manpower Programme
Fruit Development Scheme
Intensive Manuring Scheme
Soil Conservation Scheme
Intensive Vegetable Cultivation Scheme
Minor Irrigation—restoration of tanks and wells, construction of small weirs and dams
Animal Husbandry Schemes—Livestock Census, Artificial Insemination, Veterinary service
Fisheries—Construction of Fish Farms: breeding and distribution

II. *Roads*

Feeder roads, cross drainage, etc.

III. *Health and Rural Sanitation*

Health Centres, Family Planning Clinics
Drinking-Water Wells for schools and villages
Vaccinations, Maternity Centres
Applied Nutrition Programme (eggs, fish, fruit supply)

IV. *Education, Formal and Social*
>   Teachers, Buildings, School Meals, etc., for 115
>   Primary Schools
>   Pilot Scheme for Compulsory Primary Education
>   Adult Literacy Centres—one per village panchayat
>   Youth Clubs
>   Libraries, Radio Sets in villages

V. *Women's Welfare*
>   Clubs
>   Tailoring and Dressmaking Centres
>   Simple improvements to cooking and sanitation
>   equipment

VI. *Survey of Small Industries and Artisans*
>   Provision of Workshops

VII. *Joint Action with Cooperatives*
>   62 Multipurpose, 8 Milk Supply, 5 Fishermen's, and
>   18 Toddy Tappers' Societies.

CHAPTER 5

The Men Involved

I. THE VILLAGE LEVEL WORKERS

THE V.L.W.s are matriculates (10 years' education) who normally have had a two-year training course in a residential Extension Training Centre. They are mostly young, although here and there one may meet a grizzled older man, probably over 50, who has taken the course late in life, or perhaps transferred from another government service during the first rush of recruitment when the Blocks were spreading across India.

The courses we have seen were certainly practical, hard-working, and spartan—a 5.0 a.m. start, a working day stretching on to 6.0 p.m., two to three hours of field work regularly. In the earlier days the syllabus had to equip them, though simply, for very varied community development tasks for many Departments; today the emphasis on agricultural training is far heavier. They have to be able to control a pair of bullocks and carry out, to a good standard, all the main agricultural operations; to understand fertilizers and know the current orthodoxy on quantities and timing of application; to understand the principal methods of pest-control and recognize both the pest-insects and the commoner signs of bacterial or fungus disease in the main economic crops of their area. They will also have to know the credit organization and help the cultivator to fill up numerous and lengthy application forms. They are still, though in a lesser degree, maids of all work, and may find themselves engaged in family planning drives, or even a drive for getting in the Land Revenue or recovering arrears of credit-repayment. The training syllabus looks to be overloaded with technical material—more than the V.L.W. can use or remember—and in consequence teaching is instructional and didactic. More understanding of farm management and less technical cramming would probably work better.

S. C. Dube[1] prints a diary of a V.L.W.'s daily work, and it is extremely revealing. Often up at 4.30 or 5.0 a.m., he is off to start a demonstration of line-sowing or maize-planting; to check and advise on a school garden; to deliver some bags of fertilizer to a farmer; to meet the Agricultural Extension Officer and accompany him on his visits; in the evening there will be records of acreages to maintain, the diary to complete, a return of fertilizer issued to compile, a pile of credit applications to fill in—a hardworking V.L.W. has no time to spare.

His area will usually be about five villages (there are 10 V.L.W.s to a normal Block) within a five-mile radius of his home, and he will get around this on a bicycle or on foot. The population covered will be about 10,000—say 1,600 households, of which perhaps 900–1,000 will be cultivators (excluding landless labourers, full-time artisans, and many small crafts and services). In the Intensive Agricultural District areas there will be normally 20 instead of 10 V.L.W.s to the Block and the number of cultivators per V.L.W. will be considerably smaller.[2]

Most V.L.W.s have to find their own accommodation in the village, although occasionally there will be a staff house for them. His home is his office, and frequently (to his annoyance) serves as a small store of fertilizer or other supplies which he must handle. His pay, including all allowances, is normally in a range from Rs.150 to Rs.200 per month, and this means that he will live at about the level of the smaller farmers.

Most States now run refresher courses—a month or so—and up-grading courses, which last a year; the latter not only bring the officer's knowledge up to date in the fast-changing world of new varieties and new agronomic practices, but will also deepen his basic knowledge of agriculture. For a few—a very few—the new Agricultural Universities or some of the

[1] S. C. Dube, *India's Changing Villages* (Routledge & Kegan Paul, London, 1958).
[2] In fact, the I.A.D.P. areas, usually irrigated, tend to have a much higher density of population, so that the 20 V.L.W.s will each have well over half the number which is normal for the 10 V.L.W.s in a non-intensive Block.

Agricultural Colleges will offer a chance to take a degree course and gain promotion to the higher grade of Agricultural Extension Officer at Block level. There are some 60 centres in India which are running up-grading courses for V.L.W.s. In theory, they are eligible after 5 years' service in the field. In practice, 10 years is more usual, and there are now many V.L.W.s with 15 years' service and no sign of up-grading or promotion. In U.P. there are 10,000 V.L.W.s and places for 400 each year on up-grading courses, so it would take 20 years or more to cover them all; in Madhya Pradesh, with 6,580 V.L.W.s, there are only 40 places per year for up-grading, and 15 places in the Agricultural University.

It is a widespread complaint among V.L.W.s that the up-grading course usually carries no rise in rank or pay, though in some States a 'Selection Grade' does exist, with a pay differential. The official theory—typically bureaucratic—is that all V.L.W.s will one day be up-graded, and therefore the pay scale should remain unchanged. Not surprisingly, since their career prospects are so meagre, the morale and energy of V.L.W.s is apt to run on a steady downward curve, particularly in areas where agricultural potential and results are not dramatic and where supervision is poor; at worst he will end up by recording imaginary or merely tea-drinking visits in his diary and imaginary figures in his record of 'targets' achieved.[1] Some States take more trouble with this problem than others— the Director of Training in Jaipur (Rajasthan) considered V.L.W.s not far from the equal of the young graduate A.E.O.— and a sprinkling of V.L.W.s do achieve promotion, not only to A.E.O. but very occasionally to Block Development Officer grade.

Some States also bring in a certain number of progressive farmers for a short period of training (they are sometimes called *gramsahayaks*) and use them as agents of the V.L.W. for a small reward. Their principal job is to spread the use of new varieties and methods by example and advice. In U.P. it is common to find four of these chosen from each Village Panchayat area.

---

[1] The Director of one University Agricultural Economic Research Institute remarked that farm plans drawn up by V.L.W.s locally 'bear no relation to what the farmer is actually doing; the V.L.W. fills in the acreage figures and makes up the rest'.

2. AGRICULTURAL EXTENSION OFFICERS

The Agricultural Extension Officer is a graduate of an Agricultural College, quite often with an M.Sc. to his name. He is stationed at the Block level, with 10 V.L.W.s below him and about 10,000 farmers in non-intensive areas; in Blocks where the programme is more intensive there will be 2 or even 4 A.E.O.s, partially specialized in function, with 15 to 20 V.L.W.s. The A.E.O. will be expected to spend 15–20 days in the month out in the villages, of which at least 10 days should involve an overnight stay. He will travel by bicycle or bus, unless he is lucky enough to accompany the Block Development Officer in the Block jeep; in some States, e.g. Rajasthan, there is a loan scheme for A.E.O.s to purchase motor-cycles, costing about Rs.4,000, repayable over 6 years at 6% interest. His pay and allowances will be in the range Rs.250–500, according to seniority and locality.

It is noticeable that the A.E.O. has had a rather less applied training than the V.L.W., although the theoretical content is higher. Although in many States there is provision for a six-month practical and probationary training period on the job when he is first recruited, many A.E.O.s do not appear to have had it. Nor are there so many of the regular up-grading courses for A.E.O.s as there are for V.L.W.s. There are three Extension Education Institutes in India (at Rajendranagar, Anand, and Nilokheri), in addition to the Extension Division of the Pusa Institute of Agricultural Research at Delhi. These Institutes, and some of the Agricultural Universities, are now beginning to run an increasing number of courses for A.E.O.s. But it is certainly possible, though this would need closer enquiry, that some of the A.E.O.s are less practical and effective at village level than a good V.L.W.

The career prospects of the A.E.O. are, however, much better—he can rise to senior rank in the Agricultural Department if he shows the necessary energy and ability; in consequence the morale of this grade is higher.

What is true of the A.E.O.s is largely true of the other Extension staff at Block level—the Cooperative or Education or Fisheries officer. In intensive areas there is an increasing tendency to specialize, and a Block may have an A.E.O.

(Animal Husbandry), an A.E.O. (Crop Protection), and an A.E.O. (Minor Irrigation), as well as the agronomist.

The noticeable contrast with the Extension service in tropical Africa is that the Indian is a two-tier system: there is no 'Diploma' level grade between the V.L.W. and the graduate officer.[1] It is certainly arguable that this is a mistake. The Assistant Agricultural Officer or Assistant Field Officer in East Africa, with 11 years of education followed by a 3-year Diploma course on very practical lines in a Training College, is probably the equal of the Indian Agricultural College graduate and almost certainly more practically trained; and above him is the Agricultural or Field Officer with 13 years of school education, a 4-year Degree course, and in most cases a post-graduate qualification. There are difficulties in this system in Africa, since the salary differentials between the three grades are large and there is insufficient mobility between grades—i.e., the initial entry qualification counts too heavily in the subsequent career.[2] The position in India could probably be improved by a freer promotion from V.L.W. to Extension Officer on field performance and up-grading course; and a similar opportunity of promotion for the A.E.O.s into a superior scale, again based on performance and some additional training.

3. HIGHER RANKS

The staff of development Departments at District level in India, who have 15–20 Blocks to look after (150,000–200,000 farmers), certainly seem to be of high general quality, with the usual sprinkling of exceptionally good and dismally poor members. As a rash generalization, the agricultural staff seemed slightly more lively and enterprising than the staff from the Cooperatives or the engineering side, possibly because the Cooperatives suffer from constant criticism and the engineers live in a narrower world of execution rather than policy-

---

[1] The Agricultural University in Orissa (Bhubaneswar) was considering creation of an Agricultural Polytechnic to produce this middle-grade officer.

[2] For some years in East Africa the only difference in entry qualifications to the 'Certificate' 2-year course for Agricultural Assistants and that for the 'Diploma' 3-year course for Assistant Agricultural Officers was a higher grade of pass in the same secondary school-leaving examination; but the difference in starting salary was 100% of the lower scale, and the career opportunities vastly different.

making. Certainly some of the District Agricultural Officers, along with the best of the Block Development Officers, are among the best of the staff we met in India.

But the main distinction—and here the ground is firm—is that felt by the officers themselves between the Revenue Officers, members of the Indian Administrative Service (I.A.S.), led by the Collector, and all the staff of the other Departments. It is not only a sense of effortless superiority on the Revenue side and the irritation it causes among the technical staff; it is also 'the Revenue mentality' which is partly comparable to the Treasury mentality in London and includes a certain legalism, a detailed attention to regulations, financial authority, and civil service procedures, and hints of an inner access to Higher Policy. Curiously, the Collector himself is often excluded from this hostility—his assurance, ability, unquestioned position, and maturity put him *hors concours;* but it may well be otherwise with the Divisional Revenue staff, the Sub-Divisional Officers, and some others. At the top level of the State, the Secretaries to the State Government will normally be I.A.S. officers, while the Directors of Departments may well not be—occasionally, however, the Director of Agriculture will also be a general administrator (I.A.S.) and his No. 2 will be the technical man.

In good circumstances this tension is small and a matter for casual jokes without much thrust behind them. But as the development programme becomes more highly technical and scientific, the criticism of rule by amateurs and of interference by bureaucrats at lower levels can become seriously damaging to efficiency. India badly needs the I.A.S. (many other countries could do with a service even half as good), and the tremendous competition for it ensures a remarkably high quality. It is not a question of pulling the best down but of recognition of the equally high potential, and the equally important role, of the best of the technical staff. At the top level personal quality counts enough to blur distinctions; but at the middle level a highly qualified agriculturalist will keep his mouth shut in the presence of a younger and possibly ignorant member of the 'heaven-born', and this can lead to serious friction and serious errors of policy. In Pakistan the tension was stronger than in India.

4. UNIVERSITY STAFF

Large-scale intervention in Extension work by the universities is relatively new in most States of India, and is particularly marked in the seven States where an Agricultural University has been established—i.e. Punjab (Ludhiana), U.P. (Pantnagar), Orissa (Bhubaneswar), Rajasthan (Udaipur), Andhra Pradesh (Rajendranagar), Madhya Pradesh (Jabalpur), and Mysore (Bangalore). Maharashtra is proposing to establish an Agricultural University about 80 miles from Poona (where the main Agriculture Department is based); and Bihar also has plans for one. Madras, in contrast, has refused to follow the pattern, and both research and the main Agricultural College at Coimbatore remain under direct control of the Department.

Most of the university charters assign research, training, and 'Extension education' to the Agricultural University, and in the seven States where they are established the research staff and stations have been transferred to them.

The crux of policy discussion lies in how 'Extension education' is to be interpreted. Is the university to aim at taking over direct contact with the farmers throughout a State (leaving the Agricultural Department to look after supplies and services, etc.); or is it only to have a local Block as a training ground for the staff and students taking the Extension course in the university syllabus? This issue will be discussed in Chapter 6.

There is no doubt that the infusion of university staff into the agricultural development process has been a stimulant and a challenge to the Agriculture Departments. Research, riding high on the production of new high-yielding varieties, is nearer to the field staff and the farmers. The additional finance of the universities makes it possible to pour out Farmers' Bulletins; the Engineering Departments produce new experimental tools. A sprinkling of young and keen university staff appear in Blocks near the university and multiply demonstrations and training camps. These staff have a high morale at present; they are strongly supported by teams from American colleges, and they are eager to show how much they can improve on the bureaucratic routines of the government agricultural service.

They are better paid than the A.E.O.s, and have better transport and better equipment in support of them.[1]

This new—and costly—reinforcement of staff and energy will certainly help agricultural development. The questions which will have to be asked concern the integration of Departmental and university effort to avoid the overlapping and friction which is considerable and growing; and the best use of resources—for example, if the Agricultural Department in Maharashtra were given even a half of the millions of rupees which a new Agricultural University will cost, could the Department, with more staff, more transport, more well-boring machinery, more earth-moving equipment for bunds and small dams, stimulate development as much, and sooner, as the University when it is established and working? Is it possible that the training output from the best of the older Agricultural Colleges plus the seven new universities will very soon be adequate, or more than adequate, for India's needs and India's resources of recurrent revenue for salaries? This is certainly a question for both manpower and financial planners in any State (or other country) which is inclined to follow the present lead. In Mysore the surplus of graduates showed first in arts subjects; next, among engineers, of whom 3,000 are said to be unemployed (1968); and finally it is arising among agricultural graduates: there were 3,000 applications for 300 places in the 1968 intake to the Mysore Agricultural University.

[1] As an example of the detailed work one such university does, Appendix II reproduces the notes taken at Jabalpur on this subject.

PART 2

THE SYSTEM IN ACTION

CHAPTER 6

The Administrative Method and its Limitations

FIVE main tasks are set to the administrative machine of any developing country engaged in the improvement of small-holder agriculture. First, to choose and plan both the scale and the distribution of effort; second, to implement the physical investment programme and, directly or indirectly, the investment in research; third, to administer a large bureaucracy of Extension and allied services; fourth, to arrange for the supply of credit, tools, and inputs, and to assist in the off-take and marketing of produce; fifth, to reconcile the production programme both with national economic requirements and with an improvement in the incomes of individual farmers. These five tasks can be considered in turn, with an added note on the relation of university work to the government effort.

I. PLANNING AND TARGETS

The initial decisions must be based on what is technically possible within assumed financial limits, modified by what is humanly possible in farmer-response and staff performance. Apart from the direct investment in land and water, and in research, they will have to cover many external factors such as power supply to different areas and road services for access and off-take. They will also estimate the needed supply of fertilizers, chemicals, equipment, and trained personnel. All this will have to be related both to the domestic and to the export market. In cases of major new settlement or irrigation a mass of special factors such as housing, education, and health services, the economic return to farmers in the new scheme, and the training of farmers in a new agronomy will have to be assessed.

In the light of these and other[1] factors the strength and geographical extent of the possible effort, both in investment and Extension, can be decided.

All this seems obvious. But it is partial neglect of this stage which has so often led to a series of emergencies and failures in agricultural development, some of which are wrongly attributed to failure by the Extension Service or to the obstinacy of farmers. These emergencies usually relate to shortages—shortages of fertilizer or spraying equipment for the new crop, of transport to market it, of power supply to energize irrigation pumps, of staff to demonstrate new methods. Such failures arise either from bad central planning, or from failures in a single sector to meet what were reasonably planned deliveries, or (and perhaps most frequently) from an over-ambitious programme, which allows effort on a country-wide scale with resources equal only to two-thirds of the country, or engages simultaneously on half a dozen schemes which all compete for the same administrative resources.[2]

There are, of course, very real difficulties. Planning seems to involve setting certain 'targets' to be achieved over a certain time; on these targets will depend decisions, such as a decision to increase fertilizer imports. But, in contrast to industrial projects, agriculture sets peculiar difficulties in the planner's way. It is not only that the weather can totally disrupt the programme. Apart from those elements of the plan which government itself can control, the achievement of final results depends on the voluntary, unplannable choices and activities of millions of individual farmers. Professor V. M. Dandekar, in a Presidential Address to the Indian Society of Agricultural Economics, has driven home this point in some memorable phrases:

Even in respect of the so-called physical programmes, all targets are not equally meaningful. For instance, a plan target in major irrigation in the sense of creating a certain irrigation potential, has

---

[1] There will be many other factors, related to general national policy—e.g., on employment, or income distribution, or land reform; but these are beyond the scope of this book.

[2] For an example of this in Tanzania, see R. C. Chambers, 'Executive Capacity as a Scarce Resource' (Department of Government, Glasgow University). He quotes one hopeful agricultural project which was totally ruined by the sudden switching of staff to a tractor project unrelated to it.

a clear meaning; but a plan target for minor irrigation, as it includes investment decisions of individual farmers in digging wells, etc., is not equally meaningful. Targets of production and import of chemical fertilisers are meaningful; but the targets of organic manures and green manuring are worse than fiction—they deserve to be dumped into a compost pit.

Again:

We witness the District and Block agricultural officers and the Extension workers under them running around with targets of agricultural production, crop by crop, targets of areas to be sown with improved seed, targets of areas to be brought under new minor irrigation, targets of green manuring and targets of compost pits to be dug. In all these cases the officers and Extension workers know full well that what they can do in the matter of achieving these targets is extremely limited, and final decisions lie with the farmers. . . . In consequence, a make-believe world is created in which targets are determined and progress reported in terms of items over which the parties concerned have no authority or control whatsoever. No one believes in these figures, and nevertheless everyone must engage himself in so much paper-work which is worse than wasteful—it is intellectually corrupting. This must stop.[1]

Some practical illustration of the evils of target-setting at field level can be quoted from the Programme Evaluation Organisation's report *Problems of Coordination in Agricultural Programmes*:

In U.P. the [fertilizer] targets are based mainly on requirements of additional production, and as such undergo changes when the production targets are revised. The targets are usually very high, and bear no relationship to achievements in the earlier years. . . . But in the implementation of the fertiliser programme, not much importance is given either to the targets or to the production plans, which are prepared probably merely to comply with the official instructions. . . .[2]

In Baroda . . . the estimates made by the Cooperatives bear no relation to the requirements of the area or to the targets prescribed by the B.D.O. and D.A.O. [District Agricultural Officer]. However, the Societies have gained considerable experience over the

[1] Printed in the *Indian Journal of Agricultural Economics*, XXII, Jan.–Mar. 1967.
[2] Programme Evaluation Organisation, Publication No. 46 (Planning Commission, Government of India, Delhi, 1965), p. 16.

years in the distribution line. . . . Indents are continuously placed; and with good stocking arrangements the Societies have overcome the difficulties of delayed supplies. . . .[1]

In Srinagar . . . the shortfall in consumption of fertilisers was attributed to unrealistic allotments made to the Blocks, the staff of which are not themselves involved in the assessment of demand.

This [demonstration] programme is not drawn up . . . from year to year with a view to assess its impact. Nor are content and intensity organised on the basis of a review of past results. In the absence of any such rational approach, the . . . programme appears to have been mainly carried out in the Block areas for recording achievement or targets.[2]

Despite Professor Dandekar's words, and many practical illustrations of their truth, targetry does not stop. It has increased and is increasing; and it is easier to say that it ought to be diminished than to suggest the means. It is natural for the planners to pretend that they foresee the future, although it may delude them; and it suits the administrators to use targets as a measure of staff performance. The best that can be hoped is that planners will content themselves with estimates on subjects where government cannot control results; that State and District development organizations will be told how much finance they will get and what is the maximum supply of fertilizer (or power or tractors) likely to be available; and that targetry can be banned at the level of field Extension staff, except where it springs from their own initiative and from local farmers. This is no small thing to suggest; at present the whole agricultural effort in India is half mesmerized by targets of every kind.

It is worth mentioning here the antithesis to targetry embodied in the highly successful experiments made by the Shell Company at Borgo a Mozzano in Tuscany, succeeded by similar projects in Nigeria, Thailand, Portugal, and Venezuela. The essence of this approach lies in three factors. First, a very careful survey of the actual, local farming situation and its specific needs; second, almost total discretion given to the (graduate) Extension Officer to meet these needs, by technical advice related to the farm economics, the labour supply, the *local* market; third, higher technical advice and support to the

[1] *Problems of Coordination*, op. cit., p. 16.   [2] Ibid., p. 62.

Extension Officer when the problems are identified. There is, of course, a huge problem in extending these principles to a government service covering a whole country: what government would grant a local Extension Officer a year for survey and such discretion in action? Yet it is a situation towards which even government services should always be moving— an investment in the farmer's capacity to learn if the advice he gets matches his real situation. It is the extreme opposite of the central target and the national drive.

2. INVESTMENT, THE TECHNICAL PROGRAMME, AND THE FARMER

What to grow and how and where to grow it is naturally felt to be the centrepiece of agricultural change and of Extension work—although the market is in fact just as vital. But I have put environmental investment first in this title because it is so often an afterthought. The old faithful crop varieties, with high toleration of conditions and of erratic weather, are most likely to be low-yield crops; new crops of better yield and quality are virtually certain to make more precise and imperative demands on the environment. For this, investment will be needed; for example, a secure source of water must be available for new crops of higher potential but higher susceptibility to water shortage; if it is not, they will cost more to grow and yield as little or even less than the traditional varieties.

Indeed, some physical alteration of the environment which gives a new opportunity will almost always be necessary to produce change. 'Drives' and targets without such investment tend to produce premature decisions to adopt a more demanding pattern of crops before the right conditions have been really secured. In consequence, the high-yielding crop is grown with two waterings instead of the recommended four, or with 50 lb. of nitrogen per acre instead of the recommended 120 lb. In fact, much of the older canal irrigation in India was and is protective only, and not adequate for a year-round intensive agriculture. It is these incomplete changes in agronomy which, in India, pull down the average field performance of a new variety from the 2,500–3,000 kilos per acre of which it is certainly capable in farm conditions, to the 1,200 kilos or less

5

which will show up in the crop averages. Figures for per acre yields of rice (in lb.) in Thanjavur, quoted to show a sharp improvement, in fact show a disappointing rate of increase:

Yields per Acre of Rice (in lb.), Thanjavur District[1]

1956–7	1,107			1961–2	1,517		
1957–8	1,241		1st 5-year	1962–3	1,356		2nd 5-year
1958–9	1,316		average	1963–4	1,320		average
1959–60	1,339		=	1964–5	1,565		=
1960–1	1,344		1,269.	1965–6	1,340		1,419.

i.e. % increase 2nd over 1st 5-years=11·8%

The same rather moderate figures are shown by the average yields of the famous Mexican wheats in North India;[2] in both cases the crop grown in the right conditions and with the right treatment is capable of double the yield. Waterlogging, erosion, and salinity may be just as bad causes of failure, as they have been in the new irrigations in Kota District (Rajasthan),[3] in large tracts near Lucknow and Banaras, in both the Orissa and Madras river deltas, and in West Pakistan. Here again, lack of previous investment frustrates the Extension effort.

Apart from this need for much closer control of the physical environment when more demanding crops are launched, the changes which farmers are supposed to make at a single stroke are seldom sufficiently allowed for. Both the farmer's effort and skill and the administrative environment have to be much improved too. In areas where winter rain is scanty and un-certain, the change from a single, rainfed crop followed by a low-value crop of pulses if there happens to be winter rain, to a double or treble-cropping system under irrigation is enormous. It will involve very close matching of crop duration to season, possibly inter-cropping (wheat with potatoes seemed popular at Pantnagar University (U.P.) and in parts of Madhya Pradesh, and wheat with young sugar-cane is another possi-bility). It will probably involve accelerating harvesting pro-cedures, to get one crop more quickly off the ground to make

[1] *Progress of I.A.D.P., Thanjavur, 1960–1967* (Package Press, Thanjavur, 1968).
[2] Some figures are given in Chapter 7.
[3] It is roughly estimated that uncontrolled use of the new irrigation water has raised the water-table to 3 ft. in 30% of the irrigated area and to 0 ft. in another 30%—i.e., 60% is virtually waterlogged.

room for the next, and this may mean mechanization. It may well need extra labour, since watered and fertilized weeds grow faster, and harvesting and sowing must be quicker. It will need harder work by the farmer, often in what used to be a slack season employed for visits and marriages. It will also quite clearly mean more accurate and timely delivery of supplies of all kinds, and much more cash in hand, or credit in good time, to buy them.

It is clearly one of the dangers of the 'package' philosophy, involving several simultaneous changes in the farmer's methods, his credit position, his marketing, even his family arrangements, that the agency which urges him to change may not itself be capable of effecting the needed environmental changes smoothly and of giving the needed services punctually. It is the farmer who pays the price, often in hard cash, for mistakes which are made by officials or foreign advisers, and he is naturally not willing to risk too much. His experience of government efficiency is not, after all, so favourable.

The package philosophy, when closely tied to high-yielding varieties, can also lead to a tacit assumption that the farmer's job is to grow certain crops on certain acreages. But it is not: it is to manage *a farm*, a whole entity (even if fragmented), from which he and his family must live. He must live every year, even while he is changing his methods. The Agricultural Faculty of Makerere University College in Uganda recently bought a small holding of mixed farming—coffee, bananas, elephant-grass, vegetables, and a small production of milk. They installed a good average tenant, and are helping him to plan the management of this holding to maximize his income.[1] In practice, it is a very slow business. Several years will elapse in successive changes of crop and acreage in order to bring this small bit of land up to its best performance, and in each year the farmer's income has to be maintained. To walk in and tell him to grow x acres of coffee, because a coffee target has been set, neglects the complicated totality of his task of managing his farm and his financial and labour resources. This is another warning against targets and the demand for quick results.

[1] See M. Hall, *Experimental Small-Holdings for Management and Extension Use: the Kabanyolo Experiment* (Makerere Institute of Social Research, R.D.R. Paper 75, 1969).

The farmer is well aware of all this; it is on his skill both as cultivator and total manager that the whole farming revolution depends. The point is to organize the assistance of government so as to help him in the way he most needs, and to help him reliably. If we assume that government does in fact execute the investment in the physical environment efficiently, it remains to organize, through Extension, the required information on changes in techniques.

It is not necessary to cover the ground of Extension methods in detail; it has frequently been covered before. Farm visits, leaflets and radio, courses at farmer-training centres, training 'camps', demonstrations, and mobile teams, all have their place. In the end, all methods come back to personal contact with the farmer—there is plenty of evidence that radio and leaflets must be complemented by visits, because each farmer has his own peculiar problems. Demonstrations are particularly stressed in India, as a means of introducing new crops, and perhaps some special warning about them is needed. The report on 'Problems of Coordination' (p. 63), see above, is particularly critical about the way in which these are carried out:

The main considerations in planning demonstrations appear to be the fixing of their number. Hardly any attempt is made to see whether the practices etc. recommended from State or District levels are suited best to the local conditions and much less to modify them in the light of local conditions to secure better results.[1]

In Udaipur, Jullundur and Meerut the cultivators were found to be using quite a number of improved practices on the control plots also. . . . As a result, the treated demonstration plots did not show much difference in yield and the demonstration purpose was defeated.[2]

. . . the weakest part of the demonstration is the analysis of their results, the working out of their economics, and involving large bodies of cultivators in seeing and discussing them. . . . Although the farmers are convinced of the efficacy of the demonstrated practices . . . they are reluctant to adopt them on a large crop area for fear that the returns on this crop may not cover the costs of improved cultivation methods.

The relationship of Extension worker to farmer is a peculiar

---

[1] *Problems of Coordination in Agricultural Programmes*, op. cit., p. 57.
[2] Ibid., p. 58.

kind of teaching/learning situation, in which the teacher has certain kinds of information which could be useful to the learner, and has also (or should have) a method of analysis (farm accounts and economics of crops) which could also help him. The learner, on the other hand, has local experience, and experience of the task of management, and has this normally in a much higher degree than the teacher. The Extension job is essentially to pass on information and to help with analysis; it is not to tell the farmer what to do. The information may be on a host of different subjects—sowing dates, the use of fertilizers, even prospective market prices; it may include demonstration of a method, but it has to be integrated into action and farm-management by the farmer himself. Partly because head-quarters staff always think they know best what farmers should do, partly because the V.L.W.s have very simple training, the tendency in India is to draw up a list of desirable practices and hand it to the V.L.W. with instructions to persuade a maximum total of farmers to accept them.

Because new fashions eclipse the old, it might seem at first that the post-1960 programmes have been the first to make substantial changes in Indian agriculture, and the first in which a real work of Extension has been achieved. But a closer look at crops and methods in use belies this. Much-improved sugar-cane varieties were introduced and widely accepted in the Punjab in British times. Quite high-yielding varieties of wheat and of millets and paddy were developed from Indian research, and widely adopted long before the Mexican or Philippine varieties were heard of. 'Basmati' rice is, after all, world-famous; we saw one farmer (in the Tarai, U.P.) who had just harvested 55 maunds (over 2 tons) per acre of it, and sold it at a much better price than the rather soft and coarse grain of the new Philippine IR8. Indeed, it may well be true that the smaller Extension staff in the old days had more time to give technical advice than they have today, when such a huge proportion of their time is spent on credit applications, fertilizer or seed distribution, or concocting a vast number of 'farm plans' which are not always meaningful, and in any case are more helpful to the administrator than to the farmer, who knows every blade of grass on his farm already. We must think of this inflation of administrative as against technical work-load on the Extension staff as a perhaps necessary cost of a programme which seeks to raise the whole level both of technique and of cash investment for millions of farmers, not merely a few, in a very short time; but it is a real cost, and the sooner Extension can get back to its real work, the better. Estimates of the time spent on technical advice differ; but some Directors of Agriculture said that up to 60% of the V.L.W.'s time was spent on credit, supply, and non-technical or community development work, despite the official policy that 80% of his time should be devoted to 'agriculture'.

3. THE BUREAUCRACY

Perhaps more attention would be paid to the problem of running a very large field force if the difficulties of the task were more openly recognized. An Indian State of 30 million population will have 3,000 to 4,000 V.L.W.s in the field, almost evenly dispersed over about 20,000 villages, and another 2,000 officers only slightly less dispersed in about 300 Blocks—and these figures exclude clerical staff but include the Extension staff of all the relevant Departments.[1] Many of the Blocks will not have a telephone, many of the villages are not even accessible except on foot or possibly on a bicycle from the nearest hard road.

The staff are, of necessity, poorly paid; at V.L.W. level they are often considerably dependent on the goodwill of the richer or more powerful members of their village. Their prospects are not good: while obvious failure may be penalized, there is little material reward for good work under hot and trying conditions. Very much the same could be said of the lowest ranks of Extension staff in other countries of Asia and of Africa. However, at least the staff have a job, and that is not to be despised when jobs are so few.

Something could indeed be done to improve career prospects and rewards for effort: at least salary increments could be increased, since the social cost (in a technical sense) of employing otherwise unemployed young men, in whom a 10-year educational investment has been made, is very low. But the problem both of supervision and of service to staff is harder to

---

[1] Counting all grades of staff, there may be 50 employees at Block headquarters in an 'intensive' area.

solve. Targetry, and much writing of diaries, reports, and records are heavily used in India as a means of supervision. It is a bad one. The V.L.W. or Extension Officer anxious to improve his record and achieve his targets will certainly be tempted to persuade farmers to plant crops they cannot afford to cultivate properly, to accept credit they are unlikely to repay, and to adopt methods which do not suit their land, even if he resists the temptation to falsify reports, or, indeed, to accept tactful gifts in cash or kind from those seeking subsidies or licences or other favours available through the government machine. Part of the reason for using the Revenue Service for supervision, at least on the financial side, is to maintain some degree of control, rectitude, and discipline in the middle and lower ranks of the Service. A little more carrot, if not less stick, would improve matters.

As though these difficulties of control were not enough, the difficulty of servicing this dispersed force is also great. The seed or fertilizer they are supposed to distribute arrives late—the Third Evaluation Report of the Programme Evaluation Organisation mentions a case where the V.L.W.s were told to sell late seed for what price they could get and carry the loss from their own pockets.[1] They may be told to distribute a variety of plant which is wiped out by disease (e.g., Taichung Native I paddy in much of South India, or IR8 in waterlogged conditions in Thanjavur). Knapsack or power sprayers may not be available when needed; the new seed-drill which they are told to popularize may prove ineffective in farm conditions.[2] There are many reasons beyond the Extension man's control why his programme is frustrated, and this diminishes his standing with the farmer and spoils his target performance. It is no wonder that some become first fatalistic and then lazy—the remarkable fact is that so many keep up their effort year after year.

There are no simple answers to this problem, but there are ways of diminishing it. Career structure, pay, and training are one. Another may well be to restructure the service, wherever possible, so that the lowest grade of Extension officer is

[1] *Problems of Coordination*, op cit., p. 8.
[2] A particularly good example is quoted from Uganda. See Diana Hunt, *The Operation of the Progressive Farmers' Loans Scheme, in Lango District* (Makerere University College, Institute of Social Research, Kampala, 1966).

employed by the farmers whom he serves—a Cooperative, a Village Panchayat, or a Farmers' Association. There are difficulties here: the biggest farmers will tend to get most service and local jealousies or vested interests may play too big a part. But the advantages would be great—those who pay the officer would be keen to see that he earned his keep and much more able to judge his work. An alternative system would be to stop the government chain of command at the graduate officers at the Block and to use V.L.W.s under Village Panchayat control, but with government training, roughly on the analogy of the *'animateurs'* in Francophone Africa. Now that the V.L.W. is a familiar figure in India, the change would not be very great; a career opening to join the Block (government) service could be arranged for the best performers; and it is anyway possible (as in Andhra Pradesh and Maharashtra already) that the Block staff itself will become a panchayat cadre.[1]

Other possible improvements would be to substitute tasks for targets, to see that the officer is fairly frequently brought to meetings with his colleagues, and to ensure that he has a chance to talk over his problems with them and with his supervisors.

Another obvious improvement would be to give the V.L.W. a less impossible task, in terms of the number of farmers he is supposed to look after and the number of masters he is supposed to serve. It could well be argued that the number of V.L.W.s should be further increased. 10 V.L.W.s to 1 Agricultural Extension Officer looks a reasonable proportion. But at the Block level there are other officers using the V.L.W. constantly —the B.D.O. himself, the family planning organization, the Cooperative, education, irrigation, and animal husbandry staff, the panchayat officer. This may result in a proportion of 6 officers at the Block to 10 V.L.W.s in the fifty-odd villages which the Block serves; in the Intensive Areas 20 V.L.W.s will by matched by about 12 officers at Block level.[2] This hints very strongly that there are too many masters to too few V.L.W.s. If one V.L.W. was 100% agricultural, including irrigation and animal husbandry, and an additional V.L.W.

---

[1] This issue is bound up with the role of local government and is discussed again in Chapter 8.

[2] 1 B.D.O. + 4 A.E.O.s + 1 Extension Officer each for education, minor irrigation, roads or 'rural manpower', Cooperatives, women's work, panchayats, fisheries = 13. Nutrition, family planning, rural industries might be added.

was wholly 'social' (education, nutrition, family planning, rural manpower, etc.), the supervisor/worker ratio would be better and certainly the Agricultural Department would be much better served and better pleased. The training costs of V.L.W.s are fantastically low—about Rs.500 (less than £30) per man per year on a two-year course is the figure given independently in four different States; the manpower available is enormous.

Apart from the morale and efficiency of the field staff in direct contact with the farmer, the second and even harder administrative problem is to achieve some coordination of their efforts. The main reasons for putting the B.D.O. in operational charge of all Departmental officers at his level have been briefly mentioned already. In addition, it is clear that where eight or ten Extension staff share a headquarters and an area, someone must be at least their chairman; and that some one officer must be the secretary and senior executive for the Block Panchayat. It may, however, be possible to modify the degree of control he can exercise over technical staff in the development Departments. There is a considerable uneasiness in the Agricultural Departments about this, moderately expressed but widespread; and it will tend to grow as agriculture becomes more sophisticated and technically demanding.

But while technical collaboration rather than authoritarian coordination is the desirable long-run aim, it would be very unwise to underestimate the urgent need for some cure for the constant muddles which occur in the present Indian system at all levels. The report on 'Problems of Coordination', quoted above, is full of quite horrifying examples, particularly of battles between Cooperatives and Blocks and in the field of minor irrigation, where engineering staff are involved:

In Meerut and Rampur it is stipulated that 20% of the Cooperative loan should be given in the shape of fertilizers. The Development Commissioner issued a circular to this effect. But the Cooperative Department is apprehensive about the recovery of Cooperative loans given in kind. . . . Almost simultaneously . . . the Registrar of Cooperative Societies issued another circular saying that loans in kind cannot be imposed on the Societies as these are autonomous public bodies.[1]

[1] *Problems of Coordination*, op. cit., p. 23.

The B.D.O. [Chamrahuwa Block] did not allow the Block staff any leave in Dussehra and Diwali holidays, as these were the peak period for the distribution of fertilisers for the *rabi* crop. But the Cooperative supervisors closed the godowns during this period.[1]

In Baska Block . . . the panchayats were not consulted about the planning and execution of minor irrigation programmes, nor did the V.L.W.s have any knowledge of the irrigation works undertaken in their Block.[2]

In Madurai [District] . . . the general impression gathered is that there is no pooled information of what the various different Departments (P.W.D., Board of Revenue, and Block Panchayat Union) have been doing in the district in respect of minor irrigation works; much less is there any coordinated approach to minor irrigation works and their maintenance.[3]

It must be added that all these quotations related to investigations in 1964, when the production programme was still young. Some of these difficulties have been ironed out by now, and largely through the authority given to District and Block. But it is almost certainly impossible to work the complex organization in its present shape, and some quite radical suggestions for this will be made in Chapter 9.

One lesson for other countries is partly one of timing—full authority may be needed at first, to establish the necessity of coordination; but it can probably be modified into technical collaboration, under a chairman rather than a boss, when the system and its inherent necessities are familiar and understood. It is certainly worthwhile to record that, in good Blocks, the sense of team-spirit and common effort among the Block team—all young men, mostly in their 30s—was very evident and very encouraging; there is something of real value here which should not be lost. But the greater lesson lies in reorganizing and simplifying the system.

4. THE BUSINESS SIDE—SUPPLIES, CREDIT, SELLING

It is because the small farmer is economically weak, and because the supply of goods and services which he needs is scanty in a poor country, that so much of the time and effort of Extension is taken up in handling supplies of seeds, fertilizers,

---

[1] *Problems of Coordination,* op. cit., p. 22.   [2] Ibid., p. 47.   [3] Ibid., p. 45.

sprays, and credit, and in endeavouring to ensure a fair market for farm produce. The farmer with no telephone, an ox-cart in which it will take a whole day to go 7 miles to market and back, and little or no ready money in his pocket, is simply not capable of commercial farming in a modern sense unless supplies and services and credit are brought virtually to his door. Without them he will use seed from last year's crop, borrow from relatives or at 36% or more from a money-lender if he must, use only what compost he has for his crop, and sell in the harvest glut to the merchant at the farm gate. If one day his country grew richer, things would perhaps be better. At least he could buy from a range of fertilizers and sprays, and he might get delivery and even credit from the supplier; his marketing might indeed be difficult but not, at least, subject to gross exploitation. It is the stage of *general* poverty which is the trouble. Meanwhile, some help is needed; and the real choice is between help from a government bureaucracy and help from more powerful neighbours, on their terms.

At first sight this seems to leave out the obvious solution—Cooperatives, formed and managed by small farmers. But in India at least this will largely come back either to the second choice—powerful neighbours—or to failure. Daniel Thorner's study of Cooperatives in India,[1] among many others, and common observation in the field confirm that a major part of the Cooperative movement, both in India and in Pakistan, is dominated by the big farmers, businessmen, village magnates, ambitious chairmen of Block Panchayats, and the like. Some of these 'big men' Cooperatives are highly successful; in some of them even the small man gets many benefits, for which he is thankful. Some of the older Cooperatives—for example, a very lively one in Mandya District (Mysore) with twenty years of experience—provide an obvious tool for the new programmes, and have a wide range of membership. But such successes with wide social coverage are rare. Mainly the system works in favour of the big men.[2] They have the opportunity: they provide the leadership, and they reap their reward—a century

[1] Daniel Thorner, *Agricultural Cooperatives in India* (Asia Publishing House, London, 1964).
[2] It is significant that the U.P. Government has recently found it necessary to pass legislation prohibiting individual membership of more than three Cooperatives at District and State level.

or two ago in Europe this would have seemed part of the natural order of things; in a democratic India in 1969 it is the subject of much uneasy comment.

The huge extent of Cooperation in India—nearly ¼ million societies and over 25 million members—is in itself an organizational feat and may have educative and civic values quite outside commercial success or failure. But numbers certainly do not imply efficiency. There are some notable, even brilliant, achievements. In Maharashtra, Cooperatives process two-thirds of the sugar in 26 out of 40 factories, and 45% of the cotton; the 2·8 million members own 40% of Cooperative funds, totalling about £75 million. In Gujarat and Madras, Cooperation is a major economic success—Madras Cooperatives can even achieve a 97% recovery of crop loans to members. But outside these States, and perhaps Kerala, there is a fairly general consensus that not more than half the societies are viable, and a much smaller proportion are really successful. Almost always, those that succeed best are dominated by a few rich men.

It is possible to try to modify this state of affairs by injecting a good deal of bureaucratic control of Cooperatives through a Department and its Extension officers. But, on balance, the result is to get more of the worst than of the best of both worlds. The bureaucratic element carries its own characteristic rigidity with it, providing inspection rather than management skill. It does not in fact prevent domination by the powerful, though it may reduce their efficiency by interference. India has very often fallen into this trap. The evaluation reports are full of the guerrilla warfare, or at least lack of cooperative action, which goes on between Agricultural Extension staff and Cooperatives. Yet the basis of so many schemes assumes intimate and highly complex forms of common, coordinated action between them. The whole credit scheme for the high-yielding varieties programme is based on assessment and identification of needs by the V.L.W. or agricultural staff which is to be matched in great detail by the issue of crop loans through the credit Societies. The supply of seed and fertilizer involves the same relationship; loans for improvements or irrigation are suggested from the government side but executed mainly by the Cooperative banks in one form or another. Thus more than half of the 'package' really depends on Cooperative efficiency. Yet even in Maharashtra, outside the big sugar Cooperatives and certain others, in the areas of small mixed cropping there is widespread complaint (especially from the Block agricultural staff) that the Cooperative system is the weak link which constantly breaks; in many other States, where there is less supply of sophisticated commercial management, the complaints are even more widespread and severe. In most of India the Cooperatives are simply regarded by farmers as a branch of the official government organization which they are encouraged to join or indeed almost forced to join by their monopoly of credit or fertilizer supplies; or as another way in which the rich and powerful can become richer.

This is an unfortunate situation, and it has its parallel in many countries, in both Asia and Africa. The problem can be narrowed a little. There are three sets of circumstances where there is a reasonable chance of success, and three with a high probability of failure. A Cooperative of growers of a single cash-crop, closely linked to a processing plant—sugar factory, tea factory, cotton ginnery, rubber factory, etc.—has a good chance of success. A Cooperative which is marketing an export crop through a central procurement and marketing board, such as the Lint and Seed Marketing Board for cotton in Tanzania, is often viable. A Cooperative, often less formally organized as an irrigation society or a farmers' association, which uses some physical facility in common—a tube-well, store, dairy, rice-mill, etc.—may be highly successful, particularly on a small scale. The least successful Cooperatives seem to be pure credit societies; societies which attempt to market internally-consumed unprocessed crops in competition with private merchants; and Cooperatives used as a distribution system for inputs and credit,[1] especially where they have no hand in planning the production programme and little share in marketing the crop—a situation which constantly occurs in the Indian food-grain sector, and indeed in many other parts of the world.

The reasons for this classification of probable success or failure are fairly clear. Large factories are known to require

[1] The Registrar of Cooperatives in Rajasthan admitted quite frankly that Cooperatives were created by government as a tool for distribution of part of the 'package'.

professional management, and a big sugar Cooperative will usually get it; it is noticeably those Indian States with a strong business tradition which make a success of this type of work. Secondly, Cooperatives selling to a monopolistic public board have an easier time than those which must compete with the far more flexible and experienced private merchant. The consumer's pocket may suffer, but the producers' Cooperative at least succeeds. Thirdly, if fifteen farmers club together to share a well which will irrigate seventy acres, they recognize common interests and the necessity of common action—that is, they are genuinely cooperating. On the side of failure, Cooperatives which are only credit societies are really doing highly *individual*, not cooperative, business, at least in the borrower's eyes. Each individual is concerned to get his own loan, on the best terms, from what looks like an official organization—the really cooperative forms of credit are the clubs and societies, often of few members, who agree on a subscription system and periodic 'pay-outs' to individual members:[1] this is a genuine form of saving.

If these conclusions are roughly correct, the implications are: (1) not to use pure credit societies—their turnover and profit margin are too small; the credit function works best as a by-product of a successful production and marketing or processing operation, not only because margins are higher but because there are real *savings* by members, which are by far the best basis for credit; (2) not to force Cooperative marketing of internally-consumed crops where there is merchant competition; (3) not to force people into Cooperatives by grants of a monopoly of either credit or supply. If acute shortage of supply exists, a government rationing system, direct to the citizen, is less dangerous than rationing through societies. Forced membership means a majority of members who join simply to get access to rationed supplies or subsidies, who have no interest in the Cooperative as such, and who will desert or even cheat it if it suits them. Perhaps the commonest of all worries in India is the member who accepts fertilizer or seed from the Cooperative, sells his crop to the merchant, uses the cash to repay old debts or marry off his daughter, and defaults on the credit repayment to the Society.

[1] E.g., the *Esusu* Societies in West Africa, the old 'chit-funds' in South India.

As to marketing, the plain fact is in India—and much more widely throughout Asia—that the farmer so often finds more reasons to sell privately than through his Cooperative. The merchant, even if he does not offer a better price (or even quite as good), is usually ready to pay on the nail and to collect from the farm; he may even buy in advance of harvest. Moreover, he is often a creditor anyway. The cultivator gets a smaller reward, but one which suits pressing needs. He may become hopelessly indebted in course of time, and unable to escape; but until the Cooperative can match the merchant's speed and flexibility, the farmer will continue to walk into the merchant's trap, even with his eyes open.

This is not a prophecy of unrelieved gloom. Strangely enough, the way out is on the production side. If the farmer's crop is doubled or trebled by better methods and varieties, he can clear his indebtedness and meet the merchant on more even terms; and the Cooperative itself will have more chance to compete if it is composed of prosperous and competent members. Unbroken poverty is the real root of the trouble, and that must be cured on the production side, and by the growth of a far better understanding of how a commercial economy works. Just as with the early Community Development programme, the argument on Cooperatives swings back to the technical service and increased productivity: Cooperatives are far more likely to succeed in the second stage of growing prosperity, than in the first stage of weakness; and they are not necessarily or even probably the prime agent for achieving the move from weakness to strength.

The implications of this whole argument are clear, but the policy issues which they raise are extremely difficult. The state of weakness of the small farmer is a compound of semi-literacy, lack of commercial experience, lack of resources (and probably indebtedness), and dependence, aggravated by caste in India. The surrounding economy is also weak in communications of all kinds and in retail distribution—the farmer's needs are not easily met. The implication here is that putting such small farmers into a standard Cooperative institution will not cure these difficulties; and therefore some more direct action by government is needed.

Yet much of the thesis of this book concerns the need to

extricate at least the technical agricultural service from the complicated commercial business of supply and finance, and to reduce rather than increase the petty bureaucracy involved in rural development. I regard this thesis as essential.

At this stage of the argument it is enough to point to two clues which may indicate the way to a resolution of this contradiction. The first is timing. To reach the far greater freedom and autonomy which the main thesis prescribes may require a period of thrust, to break through the gravitational pull of weakness, needing a different motive power; in this stage, when government needs to penetrate directly to the small man, when local government is shaky, when Cooperatives are unable to make headway against the downward pull of their members' poverty, a much more direct and simplified policy is needed—direct administration of credit and supply, direct assistance to marketing, and a concentration on productivity. The second stage becomes possible with growing resources and knowledge among farmers; with growing political self-confidence among 'new men' elected to local councils; with growing strength of the private sector matching increased purchasing power. Greater autonomy can grow from this.

The second clue comes from a much more careful look at the tools required. First, it is not *ipso facto* necessary to involve the technical agricultural service in the commercial side of credit, supply, and marketing, nor is it *ipso facto* necessary to choose Cooperatives for this job. It is interesting that the wartime Agricultural Finance Sub-Committee in India, looking ahead to reconstruction, recommended against using Cooperatives for agricultural credit and in favour of a public corporation.[1] Taccavi loans provide another method, and there are other possible choices. Obviously, a tool is needed; it is all too easy simply to beg the question, which tool?

There is no other type of organisation which is so suited to the problems and concept of rural development. . . . It would be impossible for government's administrative machinery to deal with the numerous individuals requiring government assistance and services, including credit for raising production and productivity. Without the use of Cooperatives the number of people wanting

[1] See D. R. Gadgil, 'A Real Cooperative Commonwealth', Inaugural Address to the National Cooperative Study Forum, 6 May 1965.

government help will make dissemination of government services and assistance financially very expensive and administratively almost impossible.[1]

This quotation from a Tanzanian Government paper exactly repeats the arguments used now in India, in which the 'government tool' concept of Cooperatives is frankly admitted. I believe that, *for the breakthrough stage*, it begs the crucial question.

There are a number of specific questions of alternative organization, and some much wider implications as to the social function of Cooperatives and as to the criteria by which their 'success' or 'failure' should be judged. These must await discussion until we have looked at further evidence of the functioning of the administration and of the panchayat system in the next two chapters.

5. NATIONAL ECONOMICS AND FARM ECONOMICS

All sorts of factors influence national agricultural policy—food shortages, shortage of foreign exchange, international marketing quotas, and many more. At the other extreme of the scale, all sorts of factors influence the farmer—perhaps the most important are his own farm income, the level of work required to make it, and his security. The Extension service stands between national and individual needs and must reconcile them. In fact, the national issues tend to dominate thinking, and rightly—unsold production is useless. But they have dominated so much that the economics of the individual farm have been perilously neglected. 'Drives' and targets tend to spring from national policy, and fall on suitable and unsuitable soil indiscriminately. As examples, African farmers have often been urged to grow cotton when maize is more profitable to them, and where planting of cotton at its proper time might risk too late sowing for their vital food crop. National price policies of cheap food for urban consumers defeat crop policies in agriculture. Drives to plant sisal for

---

[1] Tanzania Government Paper No. 4 (Dar es Salaam, 1967), quoted by John S. Saul, paper to the Institute of Development Studies Conference on Social Prerequisites for Agricultural Cooperation, Stanmer House, Brighton, 1969. See also below, p. 128.

6

export on a falling market impoverish the farmers who agree to it. Tractor ploughing campaigns, unaccompanied by new weed-control techniques and mechanized harvesting, leave the family farmer in an impossible position where his labour force is unable to cope with his cultivated land. Farmers in Kerala are forced to keep land under paddy crops, for State self-sufficiency, when other crops would pay them far better.

Unluckily, the actual analysis of farm economics, complicated as it is by social factors and traditions, is extremely difficult. The attempt to analyse the multiple choices and constraints of an individual farmer ends up in highly sophisticated linear programming, which is certainly beyond the competence of the average Extension worker. It is also, unfortunately, very local. It is not usually true even in a single Indian District that a single cropping policy will work for the whole area, though there are certainly fairly large zones of the Gangetic Plain which present at least similar conditions. This means that a single recipe cannot be worked out at State headquarters where an adequate team of economists could be mustered. A major experiment under Professor Joy from the Institute of Development Studies at the University of Sussex is now starting in Bihar, with the collaboration of the State Government, to see if a linear-programming analysis of farming choices in a single flood plain could produce valid policy guidance for this zone at least, and possibly an equation in which the variables, with different values, could be filled in to cover other zones.

Meanwhile, the Extension service, with its average staffing, must work by simpler methods which can be widely taught and used. There is a slow increase of emphasis on 'Farm Management' as a study to be included, and stressed, in the initial training courses for Extension staff and in some cases in refresher courses for existing field staff; one such course is being run for A.E.O.s by Pantnagar University (U.P.). In a certain sense this could be regarded as a 'lumpy' subject—i.e., one in which, unless the full analytical method is taught, the halfway house of common sense and simple arithmetic will not be useful and may be dangerous. It is important for the progress of agriculture, for the next decade at least, that this view should not prevail. There are, in fact, large opportunities for increasing farm incomes by common-sense analysis, although the increase may fall well below the full theoretical maximum. The point now is to imbue Extension staff with a far stronger feeling that farm income, rather than production alone, is their target; and to give, both to Extension and to farmers themselves, at least some simple aids and tools of thought in approaching this problem. The very difference between successful and unsuccessful farmers who face similar problems is an indication that one is, even subconsciously, solving his equations better than the other. To make this process even a little more conscious and methodical, and to emphasize it as central to the Extension process, could now be important.

The Indian farmer of middling ability and education appears to be more conscious of farm incomes and expenditures than the comparable African—at least in East and Central Africa. The question how many rupees, net of input costs, a particular crop would earn per acre, at current prices, would now receive a ready answer from many farmers almost anywhere in India; the same question would still be greeted by a fairly blank stare in much of Africa. Probably the longer tradition of trade and of handling money in India accounts for this, as it does for the differences between West and East Africa.

The most difficult item to handle in farm management is the future level of prices—the level at harvest-time which must be guessed at sowing-time. This is a factor which the subsistence farmer can neglect, concerned as he is to grow enough food and to sell any extras simply for what he can get: 'What are prices to us? We have to fill our bellies.'[1] But it is a factor which becomes more and more crucial as capital and current investment in farm crops or animals becomes higher. In developed countries farmers have managed to force upon governments price guarantees of some kind to insure against the heaviest losses. The need for price control and support is already strongly felt in all those areas of Indian farming where high-yield and high-input costs are involved, particularly because the price of food grains is tending to fall and the price of inputs to rise. Half the Extension worker's battle would be won if he could give to

[1] This remark by some subsistence farmers in North India was made to Sir Malcolm Darling when he suggested that they would be pleased with the high grain prices then ruling.

farmers a firm guarantee of at least minimum prices at the time when crops have to be sown. The Indian Government is certainly well aware of this issue, and has recently made considerable efforts to meet it.

6. THE ROLE OF UNIVERSITIES

The mention of farm economics leads naturally to a further question: what role can universities play, as an addition or an alternative to the government Extension services? They are, after all, the natural source of economic research work, whether at macro or micro level. They might also be regarded as the natural source of fundamental work on plant-breeding, pest-control, and some parts of general agronomy and agricultural engineering. I emphasize 'fundamental' because there are certainly other claimants in the applied field—both the government Agricultural Departments and the private sector might contribute.

In regard to research alone, the university and the biggest of the private-sector firms might well be considered as the obvious agents. The university can command the greatest resources of scholarship and perhaps the highest degree of objectivity and scientific detachment. The big company can probably command the largest financial resources for research in limited fields. Government, which has constantly to justify research expenditure in competition with apparently more urgent budgetary requirements, is nearly always at a disadvantage. Moreover, bureaucracy is particularly liable to rigidity in the handling of scientific staff and especially to cheese-paring in the matter of technicians, laboratory equipment, and clerical support.

Research, however, has to lead to Extension. If the Extension work and research are controlled by different agencies, there is the real danger of a gap too wide for the spark of knowledge to cross. It could reasonably be argued that either the university or the government should control both research and Extension; arguments for a division of function need special justification.

In most developing countries with a large sector of small holders, this justification exists; indeed, it is implicit in the whole reasoning which led to the establishment of the Block system in India. There is a very large number of very small farmers; the private supply sector is weak, and in any case unattracted to the prospect of distributing relatively tiny parcels of supplies to a huge number of consumers in widely dispersed and semi-inaccessible villages. A large proportion of farmers are illiterate, and cannot be reached by trade journals, official or university bulletins, or pamphlets. These farmers have multiple needs—not only for technical advice but for supply, credit, equipment, etc. These facts together lead to a conclusion that an Extension service must be large in numbers of quite simply trained staff; that several agencies are bound to be involved, requiring close coordination; and that, particularly in the early stages, elements of control and even compulsion may be necessary in support of such campaigns as soil conservation, disease control, credit recovery, etc.; control is most easily effected by government.

These facts point clearly to the provision of a government-controlled, coordinated service, with statutory sanctions. As to the last point, it is easy to point out the ill effects on the relation between farmers and Extension staff if the latter hold powers of enforcement and policing; bureaucratic discipline can do a lot of lasting harm. But many of those who have had long practical experience of the earliest stages of agricultural reform, particularly in the fields of soil erosion and of crop and animal hygiene, have not the slightest doubt that, for a time, minimum discipline has to be imposed until the reasons for it are fully understood and accepted.[1] To eradicate foot-and-mouth disease, coffee-berry disease, swollen-shoot in cocoa, or to control over-grazing and both sheet and gully erosion, requires enforceable sanctions, just as industry requires enforceable sanctions on safety, lighting, industrial disease, and specifications for plant and equipment.

It is thus inevitable that in the early stages government services will be heavily involved in the field; and essential that

[1] The *East African Livestock Survey* (F.A.O., Rome, 1967) gives a particularly clear and reasoned argument on this subject, and significantly divides livestock policy and the nature of Extension work into three stages—the earliest stage of impact, where some compulsion is absolutely essential; the second stage of growing sophistication; and the third stage where highly trained advice from a smaller but expert Extension service is all that is needed.

their action should be closely coordinated. But it is not essential that government should also be responsible for research; it will in any case have to use university-trained staff as research directors and specialists. If it is felt that the university is better fitted to carry the research function, what is needed is the closest possible link with the executive field staff.

The establishment and charters of the new Agricultural Universities in India have created a danger of confusing these issues. Modelled on American Land Grant Colleges, these universities have been given responsibility for research, training, and 'Extension education'. In looking at their charters and at the documents issued by their Extension Departments, and in conversation with their staff, it appears that some of them are in fact aiming at taking over farmer-education from the existing system of A.E.O.s and V.L.W.s, though they are often a little coy in stating this openly:

The U.P. Agricultural University looks forward to the expansion of the extension education programme to cover the entire State in times to come. Its emphasis will be only on the educational aspects; the service and supply functions remaining with the existing agencies of the State in the public and Cooperative sector.

The *objectives* of the Extension service laid down in the Act have been further broadened and specified as follows:
(1)   To increase agricultural production in the State by carrying the results of the latest researches in crop production and allied fields *to the doors of the farmers*.[1]

Documents issued from Udaipur University (Rajasthan) strike the same note. Under the heading 'Objectives', the Directorate of Extension of the University says:

D.   To recruit, employ and develop a staff to meet the needs and interests of farm families in the State of Rajasthan as fast as is logical and finances will permit.[2]

The Punjab Agricultural University (Ludhiana) has already

[1] 'Uttar Pradesh Agricultural University, Pantnagar: Role of Agricultural Extension Service' (undated, issued to us in January 1969). My italics.
[2] 'The Objectives, Responsibilities and Scope of Extension Education', University of Udaipur, Directorate of Extension Education (undated, issued to us in December 1968).

taken over Extension education responsibility over a considerable area, and conversations in Bangalore Agricultural University (Mysore State) and Bhubaneswar (Orissa) indicate the same kind of policy. Rajendranagar (Hyderabad, A.P.) and Jabalpur (Madhya Pradesh) were more cautious.

The Vice-Chancellors of Pantnagar, Bhubaneswar, and Rajendranagar were indeed more careful, indicating that the University might take over only a few Blocks as a training-ground for the teaching staff and students in the Extension Department of the University. Pantnagar is proposing to try out alternative methods, one of which would be to post a university specialist alongside the District Agricultural Officer, while another would be to put university specialist Extension staff into Blocks.

The point of criticism in these university statements lies in the stated objectives of dealing *direct* with farmers. Obviously, if the university carries research, university staff must be in close field contact with the existing State Agricultural Extension Service. But unless there is to be total confusion, or a total take-over by the university from the State service, it is impossible to have two different agencies dealing directly with farmers. Already, in Madhya Pradesh, we found that the university was issuing technical leaflets direct to V.L.W.s and other State Extension staff, who also receive technical instruction from the Director of Agriculture.

Total take-over would not be impossible, if the university were prepared to employ some 5,000 staff in the field. But this would immediately turn the university into a bureaucratic organization indistinguishable from the existing government service. The Vice-Chancellor in Bangalore pointed out that the university was more flexible in administration; but this is an advantage of having a very small staff: it would be lost with 5,000 to control. Moreover, in States where the panchayats are taking over field staff, a third party enters the field. The Zila Parishads in Maharashtra would certainly challenge the right of a university to take over Extension education in their areas.

It may not be necessary to labour this point further. In fact, some of the university Extension directors, strongly supported by the American teams on their campus ('Any good American will tell you that Extension must be done by a university,' as one of them remarked to us), have allowed their admirable enthusiasm to run away with them. They point to the brilliant results which some of their graduate Extension staff have achieved, forgetting that these officers deal with about one-quarter of the number of farmers which a V.L.W. must handle (one-fortieth of the number for whom a graduate A.E.O. is responsible), that they are better trained and in many cases have motor-bicycles. The more tolerant State Directors of Agriculture smile at this; the less tolerant field staff are some-times (e.g. in Mysore) very angry when their work is publicly disparaged in relation to the university achievements. It hardly needs saying that U.S.A. conditions (large farms, literate farmers, strong trade journals, good roads and transport, a vigorous . and competitive private sector) contrast in every possible respect with the conditions in India and Africa.

In fact, the Agricultural Universities were lucky to come into full activity just as the 'miracle' rice and wheat strains came into India from the Rockefeller and Ford Foundation pro-grammes in Mexico and Los Banos. Pantnagar University, with 16,000 acres of first-class irrigated land in the Tarai, has developed, and with great efficiency, a huge programme of seed production, particularly in wheat. The farmers very quickly grasped the possibility of large profits, and Pantnagar became 'a place of pilgrimage'[1] for farmers (over ten thousand attended a Farmers' Fair at the University). It was natural that the new varieties, associated with the new University, should lead to much wider enthusiasm as to the role of these institu-tions, and that the small (though vital) part which a new variety plays in the total process of agricultural administration should be temporarily overestimated.

In positive terms, it is clear that, if the university carries research, taking over the government Research Stations (as is happening where there is an Agricultural University), it must also take over and if possible improve upon the existing arrange-ments for transfer of research results to field Extension staff. A paragraph from the Vice-Chancellor's Address to the Fifth Convocation at Pantnagar makes some interesting suggestions which (apart from two references to 'working directly with farmers') might well provide a model of university work 'with and through' the Extension services of the State, with specialists appointed at District level to transmit research results:

61. *Expansion of the programme:* The University is now working directly with the farmers in the Tarai area at the block level in selected blocks in districts Nainital, Budaun and Etawah and at the district level in districts Gonda, Varanasi, Aligarh, Pilibhit, Bareilly, Rampur and Farrukhabad. The central object is not to duplicate the departmental set-up, but to work with and through the extension services of the department by providing a regular flow of the results of research to the field staff and the farmers and feeding back the problems of the field into our research programme. Our extension education programme, like research and resident instruction, has been appreciated widely and there have been frequent demands by the farmers for its further extension to other areas. The University has posted only one agricultural graduate at the district level as Additional District Agricultural Officer. There is a demand for posting similar representatives of the University in the field of agricultural engineering and animal husbandry. The programme would be further strengthened during the year by adding a few more districts, extending the work in Tarai to cover the entire area included in the Tarai Seeds Development Project and posting agricultural engineers and animal husbandry specialists in selected districts.

Just as the agronomic research results are passed on, so the economic and farm-management analysis, naturally focused at a university, should be passed on in simplified form to guide Extension policy; and the same could be said of sociological work affecting the approach to farmers and the nature of any social constraints which may be acting upon them. It is in these ways, and in high-level training and seminars, that the university can distinguish its function from that of an executive State agency in the field of agricultural development.

7. THE MAIN ISSUES RAISED

Without attempting to summarize what is necessarily a complex argument, it may be helpful at this point simply to mention the main issues raised in this chapter.

The first, arising from the planning process, concerns the setting of targets—partly as to their over-optimism, which accentuates shortages and thus complicates administration; partly as to their nature, which includes uncontrollable factors within the voluntary choice of farmers; partly as to their misuse as a means of supervising staff; partly because targets and 'drives' are seldom reconciled with individual farm management.

This emphasis on farmers' autonomy leads to a second theme—the philosophy of enablement as the guiding principle of Extension. It is seen first in the priority of investment, which must so often open the door to Extension work by enabling the farmer to break away from a pattern which had its own logic. It is seen secondly in the whole range of Extension methods, seen rather as an enabling process, from which the farmer chooses ingredients, than as a package of varieties and practices pressed upon him.

The third issue concerns the management of the bureaucracy —its motivation, strength, and coordination. Two points of special weight emerge from this—first, the need and value of decisive control of varied services, balanced by the danger of destroying technical autonomy, and the timing sequence which may be appropriate here; second, the dangerous complexity of the system as it stands, illustrated from the constant break-downs which the evaluation studies record.

The need for simplification and a more careful use of administrative tools leads on to the fourth main issue—the organization needed on the commercial (credit—supply— marketing) side. Here a careful look at the real situation of the small farmer and the real conditions under which standard Cooperatives are likely to succeed (confirmed by the actual record in India) suggests a time-sequence in the first stage of which Cooperatives are not the tool of choice if a principal object is the development of the main body of small farmers. By implication, this argument suggests a simpler and more direct administration, which would incidentally make the task of coordination much more manageable.

Finally, some analysis of the role of Agricultural Universities emphasizes, from another angle, both the danger of confusing the administrative effort by a competing Extension system in direct contact with the farmer, and the prematurity of adopting an Extension method evolved for a wholly different social and economic system.

These issues are raised but not fully answered at this point, since it remains to consider the selective intensification of the system in the Intensive Agricultural District Programme, and to look more carefully at the contribution which the panchayat system may make. But it is right to say that, despite the constant difficulties and muddles, the policy of Community Development Blocks, the National Extension Service, and Panchayati Raj, embarked upon in 1952, has somehow got through to the Indian cultivator; even the small men know of it, though most of them cannot benefit from it fully. There is a new attitude among farmers. Wherever there is water, they are learning that there is money to be made from the new methods. In increasing numbers they come to the V.L.W. instead of waiting for him to visit; the bolder ones visit the university and surreptitiously pocket a few ears of grain from the new varieties.[1] Most of them will admit that it was the Extension Service, and particularly the long-suffering and much criticized V.L.W., who brought them a new hope. In turning to the I.A.D.P. story, it is worth remembering that this dramatic experience has been built upon the ideals, policies, and administrative experiments of the 1950s.

[1] At one time, in the veritable gold rush for the new Mexican wheat seed, Pantnagar University had to close their experimental plots to farmers' visits.

CHAPTER 7

The Intensive Agricultural District
Programme (I.A.D.P.)

THE now famous 'I.A.D.P.', established by the Indian Government in consultation with the Ford Foundation, has dominated Indian thinking and action in agricultural development since 1960. The essence of the policy was to choose a few Districts (originally seven, later fifteen[1]) where the prospects of a fairly dramatic agricultural breakthrough were good; the Districts chosen had to have assured water supply by irrigation and farmers who were reasonably amenable to change and initiative. In these Intensive Districts the Extension staff would be increased—the V.L.W.s from ten to twenty per Block, the A.E.O.s from one to four per Block. There would be a Project Officer at District level to coordinate the programme, and a certain addition of transport and equipment. The Foundation paid half the extra salary costs in the first seven Districts, and in addition provided in the Districts workshop facilities, an offset-printing press for Farmers' Bulletins, etc., and certain other equipment—but no American executive field staff. Within these Districts a determined effort would be made to present to the farmer a full 'package' of services—seed of improved varieties, fertilizer, plant protection, and short-term credit for their purchase were the central items of the package, to be delivered by a strengthened Extension service with better specialist advice, first at District level, later at Block level. Priority in supply of fertilizer and any other items necessary to the package was to be given, so that the programme had the best chance of success.

While the Ford Foundation was urging on this programme with its right hand, with its left it supported (with the Rockefeller Foundation) the International Rice Research Institute at

[1] Two Districts later fell out of the programme, making thirteen in all.

Los Banos (Philippines); and the Rockefeller Foundation were developing not only the improved Mexican wheats but also their corn and sorghum research programmes. It is, in a sense, chance that the administrative I.A.D.P. scheme inherited, after its first three years, a startling benefit from these research programmes in the form of much improved varieties, first of dwarf Mexican wheats, then of Philippine rice and the new hybrid maizes, sorghums, and millets.

It is difficult now to separate I.A.D.P. from the high-yielding varieties programme launched in 1967, and 'H.Y.V.' has become the title of the present Indian agricultural drives. But there is some evidence that I.A.D.P. by itself, in its earliest years, made a slow start, with an uncertain future; it was when research threw in a dramatic opportunity of advance—a dramatic opportunity to some farmers to double their incomes in a single stroke—that the I.A.D.P. scheme really took off. It succeeded more remarkably with the wheats, which were miraculously trouble-free, than with the paddy, which proved susceptible to major disease and set-backs in some areas, notably in the high-water-table delta areas such as Thanjavur and Cuttack.

It is very difficult for the visitor to form an accurate impression of the results of the I.A.D.P., or indeed of the slightly less intensive programmes in other areas; and for two reasons. First, the best yields are so far above the average yields. For paddy, the Philippine variety IR8 is easily capable of giving $2\frac{1}{2}$ tons per acre; we met one Indian cultivator in Orissa with an 8-acre holding who achieved 4 tons per acre in a single crop and 8 tons in the year; 5 tons per acre have been achieved experimentally, and even, allegedly, on a farm in Ettumanur Block, Kerala. Yet the average yields are near $1–1\frac{1}{2}$ tons in most Districts. Similarly, the Mexican wheats (e.g. S.227 'Kalyan-sona') have a potential of at least 3 tons per acre in farming conditions—several cultivators achieved over 3 tons in the Punjab in 1967/8—but the average yields are around 1 ton.[1]

Secondly, it is only by recourse to statistics that any idea of

[1] E.g. Saharanpur (U.P.): average yield Mexican 9·64 quintals per acre, local H.Y.V.s 6 quintals, traditional 'Desi' 5 quintals; Amritsar (Punjab): 11 quintals (1967/8) (Agricultural Economics Research Centre, University of Delhi, 1968).

the actual spread and weight of the I.A.D.P. in relation to Indian agriculture as a whole can be gained. The Annual Plan 1968/9 gives a coverage for the whole of India of 15 million acres for high-yielding varieties in 1967-8, and an anticipated coverage of 21 million acres[1] in 1968/9, which was probably achieved. For the I.A.D.P. Districts the Third Evaluation Report gave 3,173,000 gross cropped acres, amounting to 39% of the cropped area of the Districts concerned.[2] The crop area of India is about 336 million acres, so that I.A.D.P. cropped acres are less than 1%, and H.Y.V. acreages about 6%. It must be remembered that the Indian Government followed up the I.A.D.P. with a less intensive programme, called Intensive Agricultural *Area* Programme (I.A.A.P.) in a much larger area—over 120 Districts out of 325 in all, as against the 15 I.A.D.P. Districts. In these, the staffing level is less high (fifteen V.L.W.s and two A.E.O.s to a Block, against twenty and four in I.A.D.P. areas, or ten and one in non-intensive areas). Nor does the application of I.A.D.P. effort cover the whole District in its early years. By 1966 high-yielding varieties covered 64%, 60%, and 52% of paddy acreages in I.A.D.P. Districts Mandya, West Godavari, and Thanjavur respectively.

Within the I.A.D.P. Districts themselves there have been startling rises in inputs of fertilizer and chemical spray. For example, the distribution of nitrogenous fertilizer (in terms of ammonium sulphate) had increased from 56,000 tons in 1960/1 to 204,000 tons in 1965/6 in the first seven I.A.D.P. Districts, and from 97,000 to 335,000 tons in the fifteen Districts then working. The Punjab alone achieved a rise from 5,232 tons to 43,238 tons.[3] Similar rises in credit distribution and other items could be recorded.

However, it is far from true that these hugely increased inputs had, in total, anything like so dramatic an effect either on average yields or on average net incomes per acre for the farmers.

[1] Of which 8·5 million in paddy, 5·0 million in wheat, 7·5 million in maize, sorghum, and millet.
[2] I.A.D.P. Third Report, 1965/6 and 1966/7 (Expert Committee on Assessment and Evaluation, Ministry of Food and Agriculture, Delhi, Sept. 1967).
[3] Ford Foundation, I.A.D.P. Review of Progress and Problems (undated, ? 1967).

AVERAGE YIELD OF MAJOR FOOD GRAINS
(Quintals per Hectare)[1]

District	Crop	Before I.A.D.P. Average 1958–61	After I.A.D.P. Average 1961–5
Thanjavur	Rice	15·0	16·1
West Godavari	Rice	13·6	16·0
Shahabad	Rice	10·8	12·2
	Wheat	7·2	7·0
Raipur	Rice	9·1	9·9
Aligarh	Wheat	10·3	12·8
	Maize	4·3	8·2
Ludhiana	Wheat	11·6	19·6
	Maize	13·8	16·5
Pali	Wheat	8·7	9·5
	Maize	7·6	8·3

The only dramatic rises in the table are in Ludhiana for wheat and Aligarh for maize.

In the Saharanpur District of U.P. the Mexican wheats gave a net cash return per acre of Rs.533, against an average net return of Rs.350 from local varieties.[2] In about 25% of harvests the Mexican yields were lower than those of the local varieties. There are many reasons for this somewhat disappointing result. One certainly is that very few cultivators used the full recommended dose of fertilizer. The Delhi University report on H.Y.V. in Karnal District (Haryana) on hybrid Bajra (Kharif 1967)[3] found that only 8% of cultivators used the proper dose. The Ministry of Food and Agriculture report on H.Y.V. in eight Districts (Kharif 1966/7) remarks on the 'more or less universal failure to use the recommended dose of fertilizer', and notices that in four out of the eight Districts the H.Y.V. yields 'were not always better than the yields from local varieties'. There is universal evidence that cultivators are alarmed at the expense of the H.Y.V. crops and no doubt often compromise by halving the fertilizer dose (and their short-term indebtedness). When it is remembered that there is a risk of failure, this nervousness is understandable. 25% of those who adopted the

---

[1] I.A.D.P. Third Report, op. cit.
[2] Evaluation of H.Y.V. Programme (Rabi 1967/8) (Agricultural Economics Research Centre, University of Delhi, 1968). The return is net of physical inputs only; cost of bullocks is not taken into account.
[3] Kharif=the summer crop. Rabi=the winter crop.

high-yielding paddy in Orissa in 1967 had to abandon the crop, at an average loss of Rs.211 per acre paid for inputs, quite apart from the loss of the crop itself; in Mysore the loss was as high as Rs.372 per acre in input costs.[1]

Apart from fertilizer use, relatively few cultivators adopt the full package of practices recommended. The Second Report of the Evaluation of the High Yielding Varieties Programme (Kharif 1967) remarks that only one-fifth of cultivators adopted the four practices (seed treatment, fertilizer, plant protection, intercultivation). When all the hazards are taken into account —weather, pests, failure of an irrigation pump or canal, late planting, and relative ignorance of the cultivators of the variety they are growing for the first time—it is not surprising that yields average out rather modestly. But they almost always average higher than the old varieties, and in some areas some individuals obtain outstandingly good results. It is perhaps more encouraging than discouraging that averages are so far below potential: there are plenty of gains still to be made. Moreover, many of the cultivators who produced 'only' one ton to the acre may well have been newly equipped with a tube-well or other reliable source of water, and were previously producing four or five quintals or even less in rain-fed conditions and with the danger of nil production in bad drought years.

There is much evidence that large farmers predominate in the new programmes. The Ministry of Food and Agriculture (Economics and Statistics) report on eight Districts (1966/7) states that the average holding of participants was double that of non-participants. In Karnal District (Haryana), the Delhi University evaluation shows that, among participants, 13·6% had less than 2½ acres, and 48·6% had more than 50 acres; the small cultivators each planted only about half an acre of H.Y.V.s, the large only about five acres. In terms of yield, however, the smaller cultivators were not behind the larger ones: cultivators in Karnal in the range up to five acres averaged 32 maunds (12 quintals) of wheat per acre—as high or higher than all groups except those of three farmers in the 100–200 acre range, who averaged 35 maunds (13 quintals).

[1] 2nd Report (Kharif 1967), Evaluation of High Yielding Varieties Programme (Programme Evaluation Organisation, Government of India, August 1968).

The reasons for this predominance of larger farmers are not far to seek. There is a correlation between size of farm, education, and likelihood of adopting the new programmes. The large farmer risks less than the small farmer anyway—and there is evidence that in fact he risks a lower proportion of his total holding than does the small man in new varieties—'the area per participating cultivator in the lower size group was just about 1 acre or a little more, and that in the bigger size group in most cases around 2 acres'.[1] Further, it is easier for the V.L.W. to deal with the larger and better-educated men, and, of course, they may well have influence on smaller men in the village. They can risk more money in inputs more safely, and secure fertilizer or services more easily.

2

If we look at these programmes in terms of the work of the Extension Service, the two most heavily stressed approaches have been the 'farm plan' and the demonstration. Farm plans in this connection involve a brief description of the size and nature of the holding, of the crops at present grown, water supply if any, bullocks kept, equipment if specialized in any way. It goes on to the proposal to grow some H.Y.V. on a particular acreage—from half an acre to a large area. It is drawn up by the cultivator and the V.L.W., the V.L.W. usually writing it out. It forms a principal basis for the credit system, because upon it can be based the requirements of inputs for each cultivator; these become the basis for his individual allocation of credit, from a Primary Society if a Cooperative handles credit. Bulked together, the farm-plan demands for each Block form the basis of credit, seed, fertilizer, and spray requirements for the whole District, for which indents or estimates will be made for the next year's supply—usually the requirements for both summer (Kharif) and winter (Rabi) crops are done together. They should be completed by March and the credit and materials available by the beginning of June for the monsoon sowings. Farm plans are apt to become the subject of targetry, and we are told (Ford Foundation, 1964)

[1] Report on H.Y.V. Programme (Kharif 1966/7), Ministry of Food and Agriculture (Economics & Statistics), Delhi.

7

that 1,000,000 'farm plans' had been made in I.A.D.P. Districts by 1964.

It is, of course, the extraordinary detail and mapping of individual holdings, originally for Revenue purposes, maintained by the *patwari* and Revenue staff and kept up to date,[1] which makes such a system even conceivable. Its good effects are to make farmers think harder about their farm's future, and perhaps the occasion for making them is one when the V.L.W. can pass on useful information and suggestions. Its bad effects are the heavy expense of Extension time in collecting this mass of material (it is not as if the final allocations really fitted the plans with any accuracy at all), and probably in leading the credit institutions to expect, and then demand, a far greater mass of information than they need from a 70 % illiterate farming population. If the rate at which Extension staff are transferred—one of the perpetual sources of inefficiency—were reduced, the local officers would be able to make perfectly adequate estimates as a result of their knowledge of farmers and their year's work in the field. The passion for planning, when it involves this degree of over-organization, needs to be sharply restrained.

As to demonstrations, some criticisms have already been quoted. 'The key teaching tool is the composite result demonstration' (Ford Foundation, 1964). Demonstrations, to be visible, must be very local, and therefore immensely numerous. In consequence, the staff cannot hope to attend to them properly:

The A.E.O. of the Block, who is expected to play an important part in this programme, had not really been doing much (according to field reports) in 35 out of 38 selected Districts. . . .

Cultivators agreeing to take up demonstrations were generally provided with facilities such as free supply of improved seed, implements and also fertilisers. On account of this, demonstrations had proved quite attractive, and also led to the concentration of these repeatedly among the influential and progressive *ryots*.[2]

In the selected Blocks of Goalpara (Assam), demonstrations amounted to mere distribution of free fertilisers to some favoured

---

[1] Not always: S. S. Khera quotes cases of very serious arrears. See *District Administration in India* (Asia Publishing House, Bombay, 1964).

[2] *Study of the Use of Fertilisers and Manures in Agricultural Production* (Programme Evaluation Organisation, Government of India, Delhi, 1967), p. 99.

cultivators. . . . it was reported that result demonstrations were laid by the V.L.W. on the same cultivator's field year after year.[1]

Although quotations of this kind could cover pages, they cannot really be read as criticism of the field staff; in a Block of 100,000 population, with 10,000–15,000 farms, how many demonstrations can a single A.E.O. supervise? Further, it is beside the point to complain that the economic and other scientific implications are not analysed. These are 'composite' demonstrations, with five or six new factors introduced and compared to a single control plot—how is anyone to analyse which factor, or which factors in combination, have contributed what to the result?

This does not mean that demonstration ('seeing is believing') is useless as a method. If the V.L.W. persuades a cultivator to grow an acre by the best methods, and helps him to do so, the result will be clear enough to every farmer in the village. A village meeting to describe what it cost in inputs, what the yield was, and what help can be given to anyone willing to try, is really all that is needed. This is the routine work of Extension; the trouble and criticism arise when it is formalized into a 'Demonstration', counted into numerical targets, and then criticized as though it were a university trial-ground experiment from which scientific conclusions could be drawn. By making a target out of demonstrations, the staff are forced into doing far too many and expected to give an impossible degree of supervision to them. This analysis is borne out by investigations of how cultivators learned of or were persuaded to adopt new practices: for example, for the wheat programme in Bihar, Haryana, Punjab, Rajasthan, and U.P., 52% gave the V.L.W. as the source and another 26.5% cited 'progressive cultivators' (or 'other cultivators'); *only 5.4% cited demonstrations and 2.7%* cited the A.E.O.[2]

Criticism on the supply side is even stronger in the evaluation reports. As to seed, the multiplication and distribution system suffers from over-complexity partly by an awkward sharing of responsibility between Agriculture and Cooperatives. As to credit, there are constant complaints that the procedures are

[1] Ibid., p. 45.
[2] Evaluation Study of the High Yielding Varieties Programme (Rabi 1967/8):Wheat (Programme Evaluation Organisation, Gov. of India, Delhi, October 1968).

too slow; that the small man, limited to a ceiling of twenty times the land revenue or ten times his deposit in the Cooperative, cannot get enough for his needs; and that, since last year's credit is not finally repayable until 30 June, whole Primary Societies may still be in default in April or May, and are denied next year's allocation, or get it only in July when it is too late for the purchase of inputs. Lack of coordination between two or even more agencies in minor irrigation works has already been mentioned, and continues to be troublesome.

3

These evaluation reports are designed to point out mistakes, and a constant diet of them would give an even more false impression of failure than do the glowing reports which speak only of success. The evidence of one's eyes alone is enough to show that remarkable successes are being achieved, in some areas, by some cultivators; and that a great lift in the morale both of farmers and of the Extension Service has taken place. After all, India lifted its output of food grains from 55 million tons in 1951 to 95 million in 1968; this is a story of success, not of failure. To take one subject alone, the achievement of the Extension Service in changing fertilizer from a little-used and much-suspected object into one eagerly demanded, and the achievement of the Indian Government in building up fertilizer manufacturing capacity so fast, are both deserving of the highest praise. Some attempt must be made here to stand back from the picture and to see the main story which it tells.

In the first place, the Block system as such must be counted a success. We visited some 75 Blocks in a dozen States in India, and in the majority of them there was no mistaking the keenness and the sense of a Block team which was to be found in the relatively young staff. I.A.D.P. and I.A.A.P. have done a service in reinforcing the Blocks with additional, much-needed staff, and by bringing the more specialized services down from District to a point nearer the farmer. The main troubles at this level and at village level are that the staff are repeatedly frustrated by an over-complex system of supply and credit, and by the passion for target-setting which is often arbitrarily inflicted upon them from above. Except in more commercially

sophisticated areas there is also little doubt that the Cooperative
system, as a credit agency, as a marketing agency, and as a
supply agency for seed and fertilizer *for the small holder*, has
failed very seriously, and greatly hampers and complicates the
work of the Extension staff. I.A.D.P. has done little or nothing
to improve this situation.

At District level the picture is not so encouraging. Where the
D.C. himself is mainly attending to development work, all goes
well. But the appointment of a deputy, drawn from the Revenue
staff, is not, on the whole, acceptable, and the supervision of
Block staff by the Revenue Divisional staff is even more resented.
The development agency as a whole should be self-administered,
under the D.C. I.A.D.P. introduced the 'Project Officer', who
can be regarded almost as a District-level B.D.O. There have
been attempts to insist that the Project Officer should be made
virtually a dictator (Agricultural Development) in the District.
The most violent of these is a long memorandum from the Ford
Foundation[1] containing proposals for reorganization in Ludhiana District of a startlingly imperialistic character, in which
the Project Officer escapes totally from any control by the
Deputy Commissioner, absorbs the District Agricultural Officer
and staff, and controls the Cooperative staff; strangely, the
Deputy Commissioner is left in charge of the B.D.O.s and
V.L.W.s, who appear to be divorced from any agricultural
function.[2] The Third Evaluation Report on I.A.D.P. also suggests stronger powers for the Project Officer. On the whole, the
Indian system, which placed the point of coordination through
a single officer at Block level—i.e., as near as possible to the
point of action—seems sounder than this particular I.A.D.P.
suggestion from the Foundation. Agricultural development is
not so much a project as a way of life, involving many powerful
agencies which no one man, if not the head of the District, can
forcibly coordinate; even the B.D.O. is most successful when he
acts as a team-leader rather than an administrative boss.

On the whole then, I.A.D.P. has contributed organization-
ally not so much by altering the structure of administration as

[1] 'New Opportunities through I.A.D.P. for Growth in India's Agriculture' (Ford
Foundation, 4 Nov. 1967).
[2] The chart shows an Assistant Project Officer and 'agricultural V.L.W.s' in the
Block, not responsible to the B.D.O. or the Commissioner.

by strengthening it, both in personnel and equipment. Some positive suggestions on organization are made in Chapter 9.

In terms of production, what have been the most potent factors for progress? It is hard to resist the conclusion that irrigation and plant-breeding are the two which outweigh all others. The development of tube-wells, bore-wells, and low-lift irrigation from rivers, plus some small dams and conservation works, plus some major irrigation schemes, linked to plant varieties which, with water and fertilizer, will give both double-cropping and greatly increased yields, is at the root of the green revolution in India; the dry areas have so far benefited hardly at all from it. We asked, what could the Extension Service do for a man with seven acres of dry land and no water source? 'Space his crop more widely, cultivate three times between the rows, and pray for rain' was the answer. His yield would be perhaps three or four quintals of millet per acre. Investment in water and research on crops for dry as well as irrigated areas are the two points where future progress can be made. The exotic varieties introduced into India have given an invaluable stimulant; the Indian research organization, developing fresh varieties far more closely adapted to the wide range of Indian conditions, will produce the follow-through.[1]

Obviously, new varieties need an organization to distribute them and to teach the agronomy of their use. I.A.D.P. has infused energy into the distribution, but it certainly has not solved the problem of coordination—the string breaks on the 'package' all too often and the contents arrive in disorder. The solution may well lie, not in adding further complexity to the procedures, and not in appointing dictators, but in a clearer definition of the functions of each agency, a higher efficiency within individual agencies, and rigid control of various rogue elephants, be they Cooperatives or university Extension staff or hydraulic engineers, who enter the system without accepting its disciplines.

Nor has the I.A.D.P. experience brought a much better solution to Extension methods. Target-setting has been largely a farce. Demonstrations have been given a formality and im-

---

[1] Already, ADT.27 rice (from Adutarai in Madras State) and CO.25 (from Coimbatore) have been hugely successful; for wheats, S.227, 308, and 335, developed in Delhi and Pantnagar from the Mexican originals, are outstanding.

portance far beyond what they can carry. Still more serious, the philosophy engendered by both the I.A.D.P. and the H.Y.V. programmes has resulted in great gains to the bigger farmers on irrigated land, with a small fringe of small farmers who have exceptional energy or lucky circumstances. For the small and poor man—the vast majority of Indian farmers—the high cost of inputs for the new varieties (which will involve incurring debt), the risk of new disease, and the high uncertainty of timely supplies, are daunting risks. To lose two acres of crop is a heavy blow; to lose both the crop and Rs.700 of inputs is sheer disaster.

Thus in a broad sense the philosophy of Indian agricultural development over the last three or four years has swung to the extreme opposite of the community development, broad-front philosophy of the early 1950s. It can at present be described as a policy of introducing high-input/high-yield varieties, mainly of food grains, into irrigated areas and, *de facto*, into the bigger farms. Its positive value, which is great, is in three main directions. First, and by far the most important, it has greatly raised morale, set higher concepts of potential, altered the attitude of at least some millions of farmers, who have become eager to adopt change, and attracted some urban capital into agriculture. Secondly, it has to some extent increased the output of agriculture and helped to make self-sufficiency in food grains a possible achievement. This is a qualified statement, because it is essentially the investment in irrigation and the plant-breeding results, now followed by two favourable seasons, which has so greatly increased output. Thirdly, it has provided a trial, on a huge scale, of coordinated administration delivering a package deal to farmers. That this trial has disclosed a mass of small failures, and a single major failure of the Cooperative mechanism in most of India (as far as small farmers and mixed farming is concerned), is less important than the trial and the lessons it has taught, provided that they are learned. Many of these lessons have been suggested.

Against these positive contributions can be set certain very serious negative results. The greatest of these is social and political. There is indeed a proportion of small[1] farmers who

---

[1] Say, up to five acres in intensive, irrigated areas; up to ten acres in the more extensive, mainly wheat- and millet-growing areas.

have benefited from the I.A.D.P., I.A.A.P., and H.Y.V. programmes. But it is small. It is the farmers who were already fairly large landholders, fairly powerful, better educated, who have made the dramatic gains in Central and South India and indeed in much of the Gangetic Plain of U.P. and Bihar. The medium group of twenty-acre farmers in the Punjab, in parts of U.P. (e.g. the Tarai), are an exceptional group (as they were long before) of yeoman farmers who have been perhaps the most successful of all with the new wheats and new tube-well water. This natural tendency for the rich to get richer and for the *government* programme to be so directly aimed at them is both unmistakable and dangerous. The programme may catch well below a quarter of the farmers even in the intensive areas,[1] and it is on these that 90% of Extension efforts and visits are concentrated; in the dry areas the effort is minimal anyway. It must be seen in a context of rapidly growing absolute numbers in the farming sector, heavy unemployment, and a tendency for holdings to get smaller, most marked among the already small holdings. The sense of injustice—a sense which moves so quickly into violence—is sharply increased when some members of society are growing prosperous and most are not. History shows this position as far more dangerous than one of universal poverty.

The Indians themselves are well aware of this problem. There is anxiety about it, and in some States (e.g. in Maharashtra) some minor schemes have been devoted especially to the small farmer. In U.P. there is a 25% subsidy on pumps for farmers with less than five acres; in Madhya Pradesh there was some talk of confining Cooperatives to small farmers. But this emphasis would have to become far stronger if it is to make an effect. Looking further ahead, it could well be that, very soon, the larger progressive farmers will be able to look after themselves to a far greater extent, with an almost direct contact with highly sophisticated university research on technical subjects and on farm economics. This would release a much greater proportion of the field Extension force to concentrate, not as

---

[1] The Agricultural Production Commissioner in U.P. estimated that, for the ten million farming families in the whole State, about 2% could be classified as 'Progressive' Farmers, and about $13\frac{1}{2}$% of cultivated acreage was covered by high yielding varieties in 1968.

they now do on the biggest and best farmers but on the poor
and small. It may even mean a modification of some technical
policies. Mexican wheat needs an input of about Rs.400 per
acre; in Orissa the figure of Rs.450 per acre for Philippine
paddy was quoted, and supported in detail, as the minimum
needed for full results. But the local K.68 (a Kanpur high
yielding variety of wheat) needs much less fertilizer, only two
waterings instead of four, fewer plant-protection precautions.
Its yield is less than the best Mexicans; but it is still very much
higher than older traditional varieties. An 'intermediate
technology' of lower inputs (and therefore risks) and good
yields may be needed. The rich man can establish a grape
garden at a cost of about Rs.30,000 per acre, with a yield of
Rs.12,000–15,000 per acre per year. The poor man cannot
do this, because he cannot find, and would not dare to risk, the
initial capital. In a lesser degree, this may also be true of
ordinary field crops.

The second limitation to the current programme is the com-
parative neglect of the 'dry' (rainfed) areas, the relative weakness of research in this field, and the inadequate capital
invested in developing ground-water supplies in these areas.
One very large-scale example is in Madhya Pradesh. In a great
deal of the wheat belt of this State—for example, between
Bhopal and Jabalpur—on heavy black soils which are exceptionally hard to work in wet conditions, the traditional pattern
of agriculture is to grow no crop in the wet season (rainfall 35"
to 50"), to some extent trapping the water on bunded fields. In
early autumn the water is drained off, and wheat is grown on
residual moisture. A crop is certainly grown. In years when
there are some winter showers it may be a tolerable crop,
perhaps 7 quintals per acre.[1] But winter rains are highly un-
certain. If they do not come, the crop dries out fast—it is
sparsely sown, a poor sight to see, and it stretches over literally
some millions of acres, yielding on average about 3 quintals
(less than one-third of a ton). This is certainly a difficult problem. But since the low yield is almost wholly due to inadequate
moisture, and since no crop is grown in the rainy season (which

[1] Records of wheat yields given by the State Department of Agriculture, Bhopal,
are 7·8 million acres producing 1·9 million tons. Yield per acre (1964/5) averaged 583 lbs (2½ quintals).

is also too hot for wheat), there is clearly a glaring problem for research, both in devising a suitable summer crop (and cultivation methods and tools which are workable in the soil conditions) and in methods of supplementing what would be a reduced residual moisture in winter by storage, tube-wells, bore-wells, etc.

Similarly, in parts of Madras and Mysore States, where irrigation is mainly from very shallow and extensive 'tanks' (small lakes of impounded water), with a colossal evaporation loss in the hot weather and a huge acreage covered by water and unavailable for cropping, the development of ground-water supply by wells and pumps has still very far to go, both as a supplement and as an alternative to shallow-water storage and evaporation. The corresponding research on short-duration crops and drought-resistant crops for such areas, with their corresponding agronomic methods, is again still far behind; the admixture of animal husbandry in these areas is, of course, hampered by vegetarianism and the sacred cow.

Here again, attention is switching to these areas. The initial focus on high-potential, irrigated land in a situation of food shortage and recurrent famine was natural enough; I.A.D.P. has helped to show the answer. A new 'package of works' in addition to a package of inputs has been suggested by the Programme Evaluation Organisation. It would have to be a package of minor irrigation, bunding, tree-planting, soil/water conservation, and road access, supported by crop research, including the whole range of crop and animal husbandry suited to the area. It would also have to be accompanied by farm-management research in economic terms if it is to shift the focus from sheer food-grain production to the raising of farm incomes as the main priority.

The task of raising the whole level of Indian agriculture, with some sixty million farm families, is so enormous that it may well seem ridiculous to point out all that remains to be done. The I.A.D.P. and successor programmes have given a sense of the modern organization needed for the task, a trial run in selected areas, and a boost to morale wherever water is easily available. The Ford Foundation deserves particular credit for fitting its

---

[1] Reduced by the water demands of a summer crop.

very large financial support right into the Indian administrative system and for working so closely with it. Inevitably, if there were faults in the system, they were bound to show up in the I.A.D.P. areas. Great progress has been achieved despite these faults and within a system capable of all-India application. In future, both the Extension and, prior to it, the technical research and investment have got to be strengthened and reshaped before a viable programme for the less favoured areas and the less favoured farmers of India can be designed and executed.

CHAPTER 8

Local Participation and Local Politics

THE structure of the panchayat system at three levels has been given already. The question of how well it functions in action depends upon a prior question—what is it expected to do?

There are several things, substantially different, which such a system might be designed to achieve, and the design might be expected to differ accordingly. It should differ, also, for societies in varying stages of development. In practice a single design is usually asked to serve for several purposes and is even borrowed from inapplicable models, with the result that some purposes are well served and some badly or not at all.

The first step is to look at some of the possible purposes:

(a) *To elicit local knowledge and wishes, or to encourage self-help.* Which field is flooded in wet years, where to site a second well or a primary school, are things upon which it is wise to take local advice. Where there is controversy on such matters it may well be administratively convenient to ask a local committee to decide. In either case some channel for consultation is needed. In practice, minor consultation of this kind is seldom enough to attract a good membership into a committee or to hold its interest for long, partly because the official side talks too much and listens too little. Such a village committee can be useful in small ways, but there is no point in building two more tiers, above it, at Block and District; for the local knowledge and wishes must be really local, formed from first-hand experience of village people.

Closely allied to this purpose is that of eliciting local enthusiasm and active self-help; Community Development was mainly based on this philosophy. Again, it must be genuinely local— improvement of your *own* village is the motive for voluntary self-help. If any higher organization is needed, it is not another committee but some technical guidance in making a road or a protected water supply. This kind of enthusiasm may be vigorous for a little time, but it is usually short-lived; once the main need is met, enthusiasm for less obvious projects begins to fade away, often with jealousies that sectional interests are being met from communal effort. The best destiny for Community Development is to forget its initial capital letters and Departmental unity, and to become simply a part of an improved pattern of public and private social service.

Here again, there is not much justification for building a permanent structure of Block and District committees. In practice, in India, the element of local initiative in these matters has been much overlaid by the programmes and targets imposed from above. The Village Panchayats find themselves loaded with responsibility for planting fifty acres of high yielding varieties, or for a tube-well, or for a family planning unit without much consultation but as part of a State programme. The moment that this happens the whole ethos of community development goes out of the window; what is asked of the local committee is to fall in with a national plan, often not wholly suited to their own need or condition. Some years ago the Western Regional Government of Nigeria was asking villages, as part of community development, to put in voluntary labour on *trunk* roads which happened to pass through their village boundaries; the Government did not generate much enthusiasm for this.

The role of central government in this particular type of policy is to enable—by giving technical advice or by grants-in-aid to approved schemes; it is not to specify what is to be done. It is to provide opportunity; and if it is a real opportunity, village people will eventually grasp it.

In the 1950s in India a great deal was done in this way, particularly the obvious building—village hall, bus-shelter, well, road, school. In the 1960s, as the emphasis switched to production, voluntary work became less communal and more specialized—work for women in clubs, nutrition for expectant mothers and young children, kitchen gardens to improve diet and save expense, handicraft development, day nurseries, sometimes a panchayat fruit orchard (we saw several in Madurai District, Madras State), smokeless cooking stoves (*chulas*), piped water. In some States where the Panchayati Raj Department was energetically supervising the Blocks and villages, or where the 'Applied Nutrition' programme was adopted, we saw much of this work. In others, where the agricultural and economic programme dominated, and the D.C. and District Agricultural Officer were the main leaders, very little. In fact, and quite rightly, it is slipping into an anonymous position in social life.

(b) *To provide a means of local administration.* Where a government decides to delegate to local authorities functions which otherwise the State would have to carry out, or possibly new functions, a quite different situation arises. The local authority becomes responsible, it will usually have a right to raise some local taxation, and it usually also receives central financial aid. A multi-tier system is here obviously needed, so that functions which require a large area for efficient planning are dealt with by an authority with the necessary area of responsibility and with adequate resources. Wherever the Indian system of panchayats has executive[1] authority, it falls within this pattern. There is a distinction between routine administration—say, street-lighting—and development functions, which becomes important in this context. An authority which provides lighting, or drainage, raises the necessary money and provides the lights[2] or drains. But an authority charged with development is faced with the task of disseminating information and persuading private citizens to change their crops, or to take their cattle to an artificial insemination centre, or plan a minor irrigation scheme. This is a task of quite a different order, for which a considerable staff is necessary, and in which success cannot be guaranteed. Acute problems of coordination with government services will be raised. Moreover, the greater the funds which it commands, the greater will be the pressure from vested interests for a share in the contracts and benefits. Control of funds involves not only the possibilities of corruption, but power, and power is what politicians seek. The greater the power involved, the less possible it will be to exclude party politics from local government.

At village level, panchayats have some small funds to spend

[1] As opposed to a purely consultative role.
[2] 95% of villages in Madras are now said to have an electricity supply; but this is exceptional.

—£100–£200 per annum is a quite usual level. Though this seems little in absolute terms, it is significant in relation to average village incomes; the ordinary rural Parish Council in England, where incomes are so much higher, seldom disposes of as much. At Block level revenue is larger and considerable possiblities arise. While most of the revenue is spent on salaries of staff directly employed by the Block, something is left over for discretionary expenditure, and a bus-station or a grain-store or a new school may arise. Further, government funds and subsidies will be in some degree administered through the Block mechanism. A great number of functions are concentrated in these executive Blocks—education, health, employment, agriculture, Cooperatives, roads, irrigation may all be on the agenda for the quarterly meetings of the full panchayat and the monthly meetings of the committees. The Block chairman is a powerful figure—he shares the use of the Block jeep with the B.D.O., receives important visitors, has access to many official documents, and knows what goes on in the Block over a wide field of government policy and spending. In consequence, political parties woo him, because his power of patronage will help to bring in the vote. Moreover, where elections are indirect, and often in other cases, he will have a seat on the District Panchayat and hobnob with the great men of the District—the M.P.s, M.L.A.s, Bank chairmen, the Collector, and, of course, his fellow chairmen from other Blocks.

Finally, at District level, the majority of the States in India have held back from giving executive powers—save for Maharashtra, where the Zila Parishad is heavily financed, with a budget of many million rupees and the whole District development staff under its control. In Andhra Pradesh the chairman is extremely influential as a colleague of the D.C. on the Development Board, and in Madras the Zila Parishad meetings are important occasions, on which the staff may be heavily cross-questioned on policy matters by the elected members. But the full Council is very big, and usually meets only once in three months; unless it has working committees with real responsibility it cannot in most States exert great influence on the regular conduct of affairs. On the other hand, the Zila Parishad members do have policy decisions laid before them, they have easy access to government staff, and a good deal of personal influence and patronage: for this reason they are almost necessarily involved closely in politics.

In a 70% rural country, where rich and educated men are few and spheres of influence outside government, politics, and landowning are limited, even the Block chairman, if he is well educated, well off, and energetic, is in some ways a much bigger man than his counterpart in a developed country. Personally he may have less achievement and distinction behind him; but his position is much more exceptional. In Europe there may be some hundreds of men in an area who hold senior jobs in business or the professions or in national affairs and who have either no time or no inclination to take part in local government. In most developing countries there will be very few indeed, and this is even more true of the less differentiated economies of Africa than it is in India or Pakistan. Thus the creation of a delegated administrative system touching a wide range of economic life and handling relatively substantial funds is, both socially and politically, of much more consequence. It reinforces traditional dominance with official power, creating positions of exceptional power and great temptation; and it goes far beyond the mere purpose of 'participation' in development programmes.

(c) *To create a local political system.* In some countries, so far from wishing 'to keep politics out of development', a system of representative local government may have been deliberately installed to create and institutionalize a political system at local levels, for one of two main reasons. It may be to 'give training in democracy'. This motive, mixed with the convenience of indirect rule, was certainly present in colonial government thinking in Africa; local government was to be a first step in democratic training for a tribal society, leading eventually to central democratic institutions and, at last, independence. It has some, but relatively small, weight in independent India. India has had plenty of vigorous, though undisciplined and factional, political life for a very long time, with a larger total[1] of educated people. The object in India, in so far as it is felt, is

[1] Total of highly educated may be much more important than percentage of literacy, particularly where the unit of administration is large in population terms, so that there is a sizeable group of sophisticated men in one council.

to bring further layers of previously inert or dependent people
into a political system too dominated by the educated urban
group and inadequately weighted by the mass of farming population. Many Indians pointed out to us how new and unusual
it was to see many country people and farmers sitting on committees, poring over maps of an irrigation scheme, taking part
in the government process by the democratic route.

The assumption in India is that the political system is open,
multi-party; a quite different emphasis is given in African one-
party states. The object of local representation will be to give
firmer roots to the party, to spread a party (i.e. state) ideology
through party cells at all levels—in Tanzania down to a cell of
ten households—and (more cynically) to ensure that the
holders of power at the centre will continue to hold it. In this
situation, the tone of government will be much more overtly
political, with economic development objectives taking second
place. Such systems are not primarily designed for economic
progress, and they are in danger of having a disruptive and
retarding effect on it. There is all the difference in the world
between the balance held between the administration and local
political activity in India and that in much of tropical Africa.
It might be said that India's present main goal is development,
within a democratic (and somewhat uproarious) political system; most of Africa's main goal is the establishment of a political
system, with economic advance getting on as best it can.[1]

(d) *To effect social change.* This purpose is, of course, political
and scarcely needs a separate heading. But the emphasis is
different. It is not just a question of providing institutions for
practice in democratic government, or of strengthening political
control. It is a question of using local government machinery
to bring forward a new class of people and to modify the dominance of some traditional group. Land reform will not work
unless the tenants and landless can exert political pressure;
caste dominance (or class dominance) will not be broken unless

[1] There may be relatively stable periods, when development seems really to be
taking first place—perhaps under President Kenyatta in Kenya, perhaps in
Zambia. But in Nigeria, Ghana, Sierra Leone, Tanzania, Uganda, Sudan, Congo,
and many West African Francophone states, politics comes far ahead of development in real priorities.

the lower castes and classes are enfranchised and enabled to use their votes to change their conditions. In some degree the combination of the Reform Bill and all its sequels with the strengthening and democratization of local government in England was used to produce social change. One element of Indian government is certainly anxious to use the panchayat system for this purpose.

Thus out of four purposes analysed, the last two are overtly political, and the effort to provide delegated administration through elected organs inevitably becomes politicized as soon as real authority and finance is delegated. Only the first type— the attempt to consult local knowledge and elicit actual participation in the execution of development—can possibly remain free of politics in a party sense, although it is bound to reflect local power and leadership. Actual participation is, by its very nature, bound down to strictly village-level action; consultation may be real as high up as the Block. The attempt to expand it to higher levels changes it out of recognition. It may be convenient to label the first type 'participation' and the three others 'representative (or political) local government'.

2

How much has the panchayat system achieved, both in terms of these various purposes and in terms of helping development itself?

At the village level, the answer in both terms is broadly encouraging. The V.L.W., a young man, not necessarily of high caste or any special social standing, paid at very low rates, could have made very little progress without the Village Panchayat to support him. It is the fact that the Village Panchayat is specifically charged with development duties, that it is given at least some information, that there is a government staff both looking over its shoulder and available to assist, which has made these village leaders turn their eyes to economic subjects, widening their previous narrow concern to uphold the village order. As their messenger and contact and demonstrator the V.L.W. can use this channel, and thus development programmes are given weight in the village. In those small, whitewashed rooms in Indian villages where we have met panchayat members, there sit the village president, often a fine-faced old farmer, literate and articulate (though speaking no English), two or three others like him, then the grain-miller and the schoolteacher and perhaps two or three more villagers, one a Harijan. There will be the V.L.W., probably only 25 years old, and perhaps the local Cooperative Secretary, and with us visitors perhaps the A.E.O., a women's organizer from the Block, and our guide and mentor from the State Department of Agriculture or Community Development. We talk for an hour about high-yielding varieties and credit and why the village tube-well is out of action, subsidies for fertilizers, the rate of wages, the poultry unit, the proportion of children in school. Tea and cashew-nuts or sweetmeats appear, the president talks more vigorously, our guide translates with explanations, a young man with fluent English intervenes, the V.L.W. produces typed sheets of targets and achievements, and finally we troop off to see some upgraded cattle or a field of irrigated hybrid sorghum (and notice the bare fields alongside it); the school-children sing a nursery rhyme or a song in praise of Gandhi; many goodbyes and 'thank-you's' and we pack ourselves into the jeep and ask ourselves what it meant.

It meant that there is a known aim of development, that questions about credit or crop-spraying were meaningful, that the V.L.W. had to explain why the seed was late this year, that the village was linked, however intermittently and even in-efficiently, with an outside economic world, that some facts were recorded, that government staff had to give reasons for a failure or mistake, that educated and uneducated were meeting in some functional relationship, that new crops, a cage-wheel tractor for wet paddy-fields, or an A.I. centre for cattle, were within sight or knowledge. Naturally, the traditional part of the iceberg was not visible—indebtedness, perhaps some bribery, caste relations, faction, illiteracy, politics, and personalities. But the visible part was also real and a potent agency of change. Apart from development, a political or social process, both of involvement and of changing relations between groups and classes, was taking place.

At Block level the atmosphere is quite different. The questions are more technical and organizational, sheet upon sheet of statistics is produced, the government staff, mainly graduate, defend their departments; in some cases the Block chairman does all the talking and there is a sense that the officials keep quiet in his presence and that political leadership over officials is being hinted at. The situation is described in totals and percentages, which begin to form an opaque screen over the facts. The particular flavour differs much in different States, and in three ways. In some States the Block staff seemed younger, though keen, and the organization vaguer; it appeared that vagaries of climate and the obstinacy of tradition were dominant and that the staff were able to succeed only where there was a favourable patch of opportunity among the surrounding difficulties (parts of Rajasthan, Bihar, Orissa, U.P.). In others one had a sense of a large and quite vigorous staff trying desperately to keep an over-complex system on the rails and to tackle the whole area at once (I.A.D.P. Districts, parts of Madras, Andhra, Maharashtra, Mysore). Again, in some areas the elected Block chairman seemed a really dominant figure, with a determination to assert leadership and to use the staff, while in others the B.D.O. was quite clearly fathering and pushing a fairly weak and dependent committee along a government-directed path. Thirdly, there was a great deal of difference in the relative emphasis on production subjects or community development achievements, a relic of the change of policy around 1960 which had come through more forcibly in some States than in others.

In terms of the value of the panchayat system at Block level, it is clear that its consultative element was of considerable value—the periodic committee meetings put awkward questions to the staff, reported local failures and successes, conveyed decisions quickly to the assembled village presidents, who in turn conveyed them to the villages. On the other hand, the element of political and democratic training, whatever importance is attached to it, probably decreased development efficiency. The Block staff have enough on their hands to manage the administrative system, without the added complexity of political attitudes and manoeuvres. Moreover, many of the Block chairmen need no training in political life—they are sophisticated already. Perhaps the discipline of facts and costs and responsibility for results is good for them; but the excuses which government failures and muddles offer provide too easy an alibi: real power is felt to lie with the Collector and District officials and few Block committee members are really held responsible for success or failure in their area.

We were not able to see enough of District-level non-official working to make a judgment on it. In Maharashtra it is obviously of high importance, and would reward a special and detailed study. Except there, and in Andhra Pradesh, the impression was certainly that it was not a vital part of the machine. The District is far removed from the life of farm and village; District participation is impossible; District representative political government is, save in exceptional areas, not a development force but a political arena, to be judged by different criteria.

3

In summary, for real consultation and participation, the elected village committee is critical. It is here that the government staff really face the facts of farming, of village culture and relationships, of the actual impact of credit applications, Co-operative inefficiency, failure of canal irrigation at critical moments, shortage of supplies, price-falls in the primary markets, blight, storage, rats, flooded roads, tenancy, indebtedness, caste, faction, and all uncharitableness. It is here that the village leaders meet officials face to face and have to work out a means of living with them. It is here, in the panchayat elections, in the success of progressive farmers, in new economic and technical activities, that new classes and attitudes emerge and find means of expression.

Indirect election carries some of this reality to the Block level, and would perhaps carry more if the Block chairman was not singled out so much and the members (village presidents) had more say. It is easy for the B.D.O. to attach himself to the chairman; but the chairman is apt to be already, or to become, a political figure and to escape further and further from his origin of one village president among forty or fifty others. Nevertheless, the Block Panchayat, partly because it is stationed at the most critical of all points of coordination, is an important element. Without it the Block officials would send down their endless circulars to V.L.W.s without nearly enough contact with the tough reality V.L.W.s live with, without the criticism that a good Block Panchayat can exert with just enough threat of political weight to make the criticism stick.

Finally, in most States, the District representative system does not seem a vital part of the development procedure, and may even be a dangerous one. The D.C. is the real link between State planning and the coordination which should issue from Block level; he is able to see the organizational and policy changes which are needed, from a wide range of evidence in fifteen or twenty Blocks. He has, at District, fully competent technical advice on agriculture, irrigation, credit, supply; and he has authority. For development purposes this power at District must be single-minded and its chief obligation is efficiency. If there are other reasons for representative government for one or two million people, for the management of education and health and mainly routine administrative services, so be it; it can be organized separately. The dynamic and radical change of the agricultural economy needs, from this level, decisive coordinating action as free as possible from political influences, which have their opening to affect the balance of policy higher up, in the State parliament.

It remains to ask when, if at all, Extension staff should be transferred from a State to a local authority cadre. The decision hangs upon what seems a prior question—whether to give real and full executive authority to the local unit. If that is done, enough staff will have to go too to make the delegation real. But this prior question will itself partly hang on the issue of staff control. At village level there is every reason to make the V.L.W. a local servant, at least for the first few years of his service; he should have a likelihood of transfer to Block or government service if he works well. But at Block level the A.E.O.s and equivalent staff are graduates, far more 'modernized' than most of the village presidents on the panchayat, and both qualified and eager to rise higher. If, in some degree, the policy is concerned to change attitudes and techniques, and to break through a traditional power structure which may be conservative or even oppressive, there is a strong case to give the staff there some degree of independence. Other factors enter into the decision on executive power. But if I am right to suggest that the village level should be essentially participatory and the Block level essentially consultative at the stage which most of India has reached, and that an all-purpose executive elected body is premature at this stage, then the Block staff should remain with the government.

If we stand back a little from the Indian scene, to look at a wider range of countries and a longer stretch of time, it may be possible to put these problems in a clearer light.

Developing countries, sharing in the world-wide approval of 'democratic' political forms, have also shared the choice between the Western concept of democracy, which usually includes representative local government, and the Eastern recipe of 'People's Democracies', based on a dominant party supposedly representing popular will. Ex-colonies—the majority of developing countries—may seem to have been reacting against the authoritarian nature of colonial rule. But in certain ways this is a superficial judgment. Beneath the colonial overlay were societies in very different stages. Some had already developed, through conquest or evolution, an authoritarian and hierarchical structure—the Fulani Empire, Buganda, India; some were a collection of tribes, strung together as a colonial state but without organic unity and often without authoritarian local forms.

At Independence, the authoritarian systems emerged to face the same problem as uncolonized countries such as Thailand, Afghanistan, Iran—a need to democratize a system in which authoritarianism was in fact organic. What may be called the tribal systems faced a rather different issue—the creation of a democratic system without passing through an authoritarian stage.

Very broadly, the results may be divided into three main patterns (with many variants in each). Some chose the People's Democracy, to Western eyes a highly authoritarian system in disguise; some, the pattern of Western representative government; some a compromise, in which the colonial type of provincial and district administration was retained, to unify and control, but modified by a political element—politicians as regional commissioners and a party system constituting central government.

In some degree, all systems of local councils reflect one of these three political choices, and their evolution is a matter for study by political scientists. But the requirement of development is a different matter altogether. What we have been describing is an attempt to use systems of largely political origin for development purposes, and to use them within societies at very different stages of organic political tradition.

In some cases the distinction is clear even in today's structures. 'Self-help' committees, and the whole community development movement belong to the development philosophy; county councils, etc., belong to the Western political reform. The Indian panchayats are an amalgam, in which political idealism ('Panchayati Raj') and development aims (National Extension Blocks) are almost totally fused.

Much of this book has emphasized that, for agricultural development, a high degree of local discretion, initiative, and adaptation to the local environment is needed. Thus the question is whether this is to be achieved by local representation (inevitably political), or by an elaborate official system of help, of coaching local people to take their own decisions, and, above all, of enabling them to do so by investment, services, and technical aid.

At certain stages of growth, and within certain historical traditions, the people themselves may at first prefer a paternalist, official approach. It is significant that over 55% of the sample of Indian villagers preferred unanimous elections to panchayats.[1] Arthur Gaitskell, in his book on the Gezira cotton scheme, records the first reaction of the growers to suggestions that they should take decisions by democratic means: 'You decide for us: we shall only quarrel among ourselves.' This short remark has significance for hundreds of situations all over the world. It probably springs from two causes—unwillingness to risk the increase of faction in societies where social unity has been essential to survival, and a long-established adaptation to authoritarian government and values. It must be added that the Gezira Board persisted in their policy, and, after a period of exaggerated democratic reaction[2] in which officials were rejected, finally achieved a tolerable balance.

[1] See above, p. 42, n. 1.
[2] Possibly a reaction to rejection by the official 'father', as Mannoni suggested in his studies of Madagascar: O. Mannoni, *Prospero and Caliban* (Methuen, London, 1956).

Thus countries with an indigenous authoritarian background and large areas of traditional, semi-subsistence local communities may have to proceed slowly and carefully in democratization. The cautious arrangements in India, by which the D.C. retains executive powers, or a veto, or a guiding hand on the elected councils, show exactly this compromise. It is one which is at once nursing rather nervous communities into greater self-confidence, holding the ring for them, so that the new democratic forms are not captured by the old authoritarian leadership, and providing a channel for investment and technical services. Countries with a tribal background may well have been wise in retaining a colonial-type local administration complemented by self-help committees but not yet by Local Government. Countries which have chosen the People's Democracy pattern may find that the authoritarianism of the party, which very easily produces both faction and uncertainty in the village, turns out to be both politically the hardest to manage and economically the least conducive to development, since it is the least tolerant of the discipline which investment and technical aid demand.

PART 3

REVIEW

CHAPTER 9

Suggestions, Comparisons, Conclusions

THE object of studying the Indian experience of agricultural development was not primarily to suggest amendments to the Indian system. Some suggestions have indeed been made; but India has no lack of more knowledgeable and able critics to improve upon them. It was to draw from it some general conclusions which might be applied more widely in the developing world. Propositions based upon some condition in which India is unique must obviously be excluded; but the range of conditions in India is great, and many vital factors—poverty, illiteracy, small holdings, for example—are common to large areas of the developing world.

I. STAGES OF GROWTH

A consultant to a country, called upon to advise on agricultural development, would start by getting into his mind a general picture of the society which he was entering—population, land resources; traditional structure, ethical and religious values, education; production and employment, budgetary resources, development potential; existing political, social, and economic institutions, and dominant political ideals. For this picture to be orderly and meaningful, it would have to be related to some concept of the stage of maturity this society had reached, defining maturity in terms of a 'modern' society. 'Modern' maturity here would imply a high general level of education, a general use of developed technology, a political structure able to provide an adequate degree of social and economic control, a high degree of personal liberty, and some defensible level of justice in the distribution of wealth and benefits.[1] By contrasting this ideal with the actual situation, he would begin to sketch out mentally the path of growth which such a society could take, distinguishing most sharply between the steps which might be taken at once and those which might become possible later. Since social factors are linked, the consultant would probably carry in his mind, consciously or unconsciously, a rough typology of societies at various stages on the path of growth. Rough it must be, because the circumstances and genius of each country will give it a unique flavour. This is only common sense. It is the attempt to refine this concept, to see in far more precision and detail the interdependencies between the state of literacy the, political institutions, the social structure and income distribution, the technology in common use, and the quality of administration, and to distinguish more carefully between immediate and distant solutions, which will make the difference between good and bad advice.

The government of a nation, if it is well-intentioned, is in the position of this consultant, but with power to act. It is in the pre-planning stage that decisions which have a real claim to be called policy decisions have to be made. If they are not made rationally, it is probably because government is not well-intentioned but interested mainly in its own preservation or in cutting a dash in the world. If they are not made at all, it may be because they imply limitations which governments are loth to face. They are, however, especially important for the agricultural or pastoral economy because it is the most traditional sector, where techniques and institutions need to be most carefully matched to the stage of social and economic change. To treat the small farmer, whether customary holder, or tenant, or owner, with his four or five acres of fragmented holding, with little or no schooling, with perhaps a burden of debt and certainly a family to support, as though he could use banks, manage a Cooperative, sit effectively on a local council, risk half a year's income on expensive inputs, change his secure method of cultivation for a new and risky one (even if the

---

[1] There are some obvious value judgments here. It is assumed, for example, that few people would regard as 'mature' a society consisting mainly of millionaires and starving paupers. The most fundamental cultural and religious values are omitted: they may characterize any stage of society, including the most undeveloped, and (alas) certainly do not enter into the usual definitions of modernity.

promised reward is higher), is to behave unreasonably. Yet in time, perhaps not much more than a decade or two later, he will be able to do all these things. Society has to grow; it has to learn to walk before it can run. The pre-planning decision of what is appropriate and timely for growth precedes in time and significance the planning decision of how much can be done; and some of these pre-planning decisions must be changed from time to time, as society changes and can manage more demanding tasks.

2. SOCIAL PHILOSOPHY

'Dominant political ideals' were included as one factor in the pre-planning data, and in this sphere a vital question has so far been begged. It has been assumed that a government will aim at some degree of social equality, at least in income distribution; for this reason a policy of raising the level of the small farmer's life has been included, indeed emphasized, in this study of Extension.

This question is sometimes discussed as a moral issue, and sometimes purely as a practical one. On practical grounds, it can be argued that the most speedy route to equality is to start by backing the relatively rich and enterprising, who will be most capable of generating economic growth, later to be diffused either through impersonal economic forces or by conscious social policy. This argument is supported by metaphors about making a larger cake rather than dividing a small one equally; or by arguments that more productive methods will be diffused most quickly through the example of pioneers rather than by a broad-front attack; it could also be argued that developing countries cannot deploy administrative resources adequate to make such a broad attack. The opposite point of view has also both a moral and a practical dimension. The practical grounds here will be a prophecy that to increase inequality, if only temporarily, will lead to political upheavals so violent as to halt economic growth, or at least to destroy the present holders of power. There are also respectable economic arguments that more equal income distribution would accelerate growth in some developing countries.

This issue can be very easily brought down from the realm

of general argument to some extremely detailed issues and decisions. For example, it has been assumed here that it is a 'bad' thing for Cooperatives to be too completely dominated by the bigger and richer farmers and merchants; and this is consistent with Indian policy, which has so far been professedly egalitarian. But it could well be argued that, in the transition to a commercial economy, some men—a minority—are bound to emerge from the ruck, men with more vision or energy or cunning, or simply a privileged start in the race, and that this emergence is inevitable in one form or another; if they do not appear through Cooperatives, they will appear as dominants in a party hierarchy, or in any sphere where the rewards—whether of money or power—are tempting. In the study of Co-operation in Tanzania by J. S. Saul already quoted, the mounting anxiety of the Tanzanian Government on this score is admirably brought out. The Tanzanian Cooperatives have in fact offered an opportunity for corruption and personal gain in power and money to the 'activists' who first emerged from the traditional society. Thus the very vehicle of socialist advance favoured by the Tanzanian Government, as an alternative to capitalism and greedy middlemen, is in danger of turning into a vehicle of inequality and even exploitation by producers.

The issue is quite clearly vital to the whole consideration of general rural development; it perhaps underlies the crisis between 'conservatism' and 'socialism' evidenced in the split in the Indian Congress between Mrs. Gandhi and her opponents.

It is obviously impossible to suggest 'solutions', but it is per-haps desirable to indicate, in a few sentences, the assumptions on which this study rests. They are, in brief, that in each suc-ceeding stage of social growth human energy will break through the current norms into types of behaviour which carry both possibilities of economic and technical advance and possibilities of unacceptable injustice and abuse. The moral discipline has to be evolved, *pari passu*; too much may lead to stagnation, too little to revolution. 'It is in the translation of morals into politics that human progress consists.'[1] Big men are bound to dominate Cooperatives (or any other local institution where the majority of members are poor and illiterate) in one way or

---

[1] Pareto.

another; the point is to modify the results of this in two ways—by controlling their excesses and (more importantly) by enabling smaller men to compete and share in the process of control. 'Maturity', in fact, is a misnomer; each society has to find the disciplines for its own stage of advancing energy and techniques—perhaps most of all the present developed societies. The concept of stages here refers to the disciplines appropriate to successive points of this unfinished sequence.

In practical application, if we continue the example from Cooperatives, there are parts of India where any genuine share of control by small men is virtually impossible, partly from general ignorance and poverty but also because the big men have so many strings to their bow of domination—caste, land ownership, their position as both creditors and political bosses. In such cases the institution of Cooperation may not even be progressive: 'new men' will never get a chance to emerge. There are other areas where prosperity and commercial knowledge are more widely spread, where Cooperatives may actually foster the emergence of new energies in new classes; in these a modicum of discipline and of special attention to the weaker elements may be all that is needed to secure both growth and at least a reasonable degree of social justice; an exactly parallel argument applies to elected local councils.

This book may give an impression of hostility to 'big' men. This would be unjust to many of them. Some, indeed, are young, educated men who have shown admirable energy in developing new crops and new commercial openings, and shared their knowledge widely. Some of the older men have maintained the best kind of paternalism towards tenants and neighbours, who have gladly benefited from it. The point of criticism is not directed against the big men but against the lack of opportunity for small men. In Indian agricultural development over the last ten years egalitarian philosophy has been somewhat smothered by traditional practice. The rewards have gone mostly to the strong; there has been some dramatic growth and some dramatic inequality. In socialist Africa there has been a tendency to put on the brakes of moral discipline before growth achieved any momentum. It is interesting that energy has in consequence broken out in oblique and sometimes equally undesirable ways.

9

3. PLANNING AND INVESTMENT

Good agriculture in a temperate zone—in England or France, for example—looks so 'natural' to the layman that the huge investment which has been made in those cornfields and pastures and wandering roads is easy to forget, partly because it is not obtrusive, partly because it has been done over so many centuries—drainage, levelling, river training, power supply, access, shelter, storage, and behind it all a large engineering and chemical industry. In developing countries the concept of investment has been perhaps unduly concentrated on dramatic schemes of major irrigation or forest clearance. Yet at some stage this control of the environment has to be achieved. Huge rivers, which cause floods or waste their water in the oceans, have to be tamed, and that is a slow and expensive business; the same applies often enough to unproductive forest or 'bush'. In Africa there is a great deal of wild and difficult country, and—for example, in Uganda—the small clearances and rough fields are often to this day surrounded by rampant elephant-grass or bush; the rivers roar down in flood and the roads become impassable. Much of Asia was tamed earlier—the level fields or terraces show it: paddy is growing where swamp or forest stood, and the marvellous wheat-fields of the Tarai below the Himalayas were the haunt of tigers even within living memory.[1]

But in parallel with these major attacks on the environment, a veritable host of smaller investments and skills are needed, which will one day give the 'natural' look to a high level of farming. If there is one thing that the Indian experience has underlined, it is that a further step in agricultural advance has owed more to investment than to organization or propaganda or literacy or Cooperatives or community development. The two critical investments have been in water supply and crop research, applied to a skilled tradition of farming. All the other factors—they are necessary factors—have followed on these, and without these the rest have been very largely ineffective. In tropical Africa land clearance, an earlier stage, is as important as water supply in many areas.

[1] One prosperous farmer told us that he had seen two tigers walking round the first clearing of his farm.

Water supply, in agricultural terms, is an expensive business, even when major irrigation is not involved. Geological, hydrological, and soil survey are necessary if the job is to be done properly. If the water is there, a great deal of land-shaping will be needed to use it well. Drainage is as necessary as supply, as India and Pakistan have learned to their real cost in millions of acres of salinity and millions of rupees in reclamation. Research is also costly, when all its stages are counted in—fundamental work in plant-breeding, followed by work on agronomy, followed by local testing, rebreeding for local conditions, developing an economic regime of fertilization, pest-control, sowing dates, water management, and so on, and followed again by staff training and farmer training.

Extension comes very late in this sequence, with all the associated organizational and supply and marketing problems which go with it; and success in Extension depends on the prior investment. There are, indeed, some places where existing knowledge and proven practices can be extended far more widely—the spread of both coffee and tea to African small holders in Kenya is an example. There are places where a social change—land use in particular—can achieve dramatic results. But in those areas, and they are probably the largest, where the effort to improve agriculture has been applied for many decades without notable success, something new has to be done, in physical investment or research or both together, before results are likely. If in India the Extension Service has often been frustrated by failures in organization or supply or credit or marketing, nevertheless the lack of investment and research is, over millions of acres, much more significant. Quite a lot of the agricultural budget in Extension salaries and administration is thrown away in keeping a staff hammering vainly at a door of agricultural advance which can only be unlocked by these two factors.[1] It is here that national economic planning, followed by detailed agricultural planning, has so much to give.

To these decisions on investment the normal planning considerations of recurrent expenditure and taxation, levels of consumption, and the production or import of consumption

[1] I am not forgetting that massive investment can in turn be wasted for lack of Extension. Huge sums have been spent in Thailand on dams and reservoirs before there had been any education of the farmers in irrigated agriculture.

goods will be added. The result will be estimates both of investment and of the recurrent effort, in terms of staff and supplies, which can go into the agricultural sector. It remains to say that Aid can be added (with adjustments) to the investment programme, and Aid is, or could be, particularly significant in the difficult fields of survey and research.

4. THE AGENCIES

Where the appropriateness of effort, its scale, and its timing have been decided, and when the investment programme has been planned, the question of agencies to effect change comes next. This is essentially a social problem, and the critical issue is therefore that of appropriateness to the existing society. Agriculture in developed countries is essentially self-running save for the price mechanism, which is usually much regulated by government. There is, indeed, an important technical input from government and universities, in staff and especially in research; but the private industrial and credit structure does virtually the whole job of laying before the farmer a choice of materials, equipment of all kinds, and finance, and farming decisions are made by the farmer's selection. In socialist, centrally planned economies this range of supply may come from government rather than from a free market, but it fulfils the same role—the question whether a tractor manufacturing industry should be run by the state or by private enterprise goes far beyond this study.

But in developing countries this whole environment of plentiful services and choices does not exist—this is almost a definition of their situation. Thus the choice of agency to provide it, in gradually increasing volume, becomes critical. Most critical of all is the precise definition of the stage of development which a particular economy, and particular regions and districts of that economy, have reached. To go straight to an example, I.A.D.P. in India is a programme which demands a quite high degree of precision, in the timing of supplies of all kinds for double or treble-cropping, in agronomy, in the supply and repayment of credit. It is applied to an economy in which, for example, most villages have no telephone; an infinitesimal proportion of farmers have a car; private distribution of tools, fertilizer, spares, etc., etc., barely goes beyond small market towns. If a farmer needs urgently a bag of fertilizer, a spray for some sudden onslaught of crop disease, a spare part for his pump at a critical moment for watering his crop, his only resource may be to go in a bullock cart to town for it, which will take a day and may easily prove fruitless—a job which a telephone call or half-an-hour in a car will do in England. Most parts of tropical Africa are much worse off, both in administration and facilities.

It therefore becomes important to ask if I.A.D.P. is the appropriate programme for the conditions. In fact, it relies partly on a bureaucracy to manage this multifarious problem of quick and accurate supply and support, and the bureaucracy almost inevitably ties itself in more and more complex knots in the attempt to do it. It is natural that its successes are greater among those farmers who can, in effect, exert an exceptional command over the scanty services available; who can afford to stock up with materials, who can reach a telephone or bully an official to organize supply. It succeeds also within those 'islands' of developed economic relationships which big production companies or corporations build up around themselves, with telephone, transport, storage, credit, professional management, all financed out of a large-scale operation: the productive labour force is then fully and accurately serviced. It only succeeds at all with the small village farmer by an almost miraculous outcome of constantly renewed effort and persistence by an administration fighting its way through the cat's-cradle of its own systems.

Much the same situation applies to Cooperative action. Where there are educated and influential leaders, who are at home in a commercial economy and provide both management skill and an effective call on resources, the Cooperative may work well, though not always justly. The Cooperatives of very small and uninfluential farmers, dependent on a system of supply and credit over which they have little influence, are highly likely to fail. In general, tropical Africa is much worse placed than Asia in this respect—the tradition of commerce is far less developed, the supply system is generally weaker, the farming population, though sometimes highly skilled in their own traditional speciality, is more uniformly poor; there are many more relatively rich and educated farmers scattered through the Indian countryside than there are in tropical Africa, except perhaps among Ghana cocoa-farmers and a very few other groups.

The provision of credit leads to much the same argument. Most very backward small farmers are intrinsically uncredit-worthy, partly because their whole income and cash position is shaky and unsound as a family unit—deaths, marriages, illness, unfavourable weather, etc., can totally destroy their viability—and partly because the way in which they apply credit seldom produces the net gain in earnings which allows both for profit and repayment. Credit applied by a larger unit—as a sugar company may supply fertilizer and crop protection to out-growers—means that the crop decision and the profitability calculation is made by a competent body, and recovery is made on a scale large enough to cover a small proportion of chance failures. Since nearly all government-backed credit schemes to small farmers, whether channelled through Cooperatives or the administration, lose quite a lot of money,[1] it might be better to spend the money on a competent mangement unit for as long as was necessary to get it onto its feet.

The argument is pointing more and more strongly to a need for competent leadership and management of groups of farmers, on a quite local scale but big enough in acreage and turnover to justify the management cost. It is reinforced by experience which has not been sufficiently heeded—the experi-ence of voluntary agencies who have set themselves to improve farming either for its own sake or as part of some other project or institution. There are literally hundreds of such examples in developing countries—missions, schools, nutrition projects, relief and settlement schemes. An excellent sample of such schemes in East Africa, recording both difficulties and achieve-ments, has recently been published.[2] Characteristically, the agency gains the confidence of local farmers, bringing them

[1] In about 1960 the Northern Nigerian Government made available £900,000 for credit to farmers. Only about £400,000 of this was recovered.

[2] Report of a conference organized by the Department of Rural Economy and Extension, Makerere University College (Uganda), and held at the Social Centre, Kikuyu (Kenya), in 1967, financed by UNICEF. The conference brought to-gether representatives of voluntary agencies, mainly Christian, throughout East Africa. Agricultural schemes included two from leprosy settlements, one from

technical advice and help both in growing and selling their crop; those based on institutions may also include some common equipment or facility (storage, transport, a dairy, etc.). Very few are organized as formal Cooperatives. Almost invariably the result is a marked step forward in agricultural productivity, often well ahead of neighbouring areas where the regular government Extension Service—and perhaps standard Cooperatives—are functioning. Once again, the Shell principles of local knowledge, discretion, and support come in.

The virtues of these projects seem to lie in their flexible adaptation to local needs: the fact that they are not forced into a national pattern either of production policy or of organization; and that their funds, although usually very meagre, are freely disposable at the discretion of the local unit—if a lorry or a well or a cold store is what is most urgently needed, the money is spent on it. Their weakness may lie in the technical training of their staff, but it is largely compensated by a lower number of farm families per Extension worker and by the ability to call on technical advice if it is needed.

This field experience, as regards organization, is increasingly underlined by more academic studies. It has been pointed out by Professor R. P. Dore[1] that, because a traditional society has certain elements of solidarity and cooperative effort, it does *not* necessarily take to modern Cooperatives like a duck to water; the structure, purpose, sanctions, and cultural style of traditional mutual aid or communitarian activity are wholly different from those of formal Cooperatives. J. M. Texier,[2] confirming this, has pointed out that some two hundred different types of 'para-Cooperative' or 'pre-Cooperative' structures have been found or tried out in various countries—pre-Cooperatives have

---

[1] R. P. Dore, 'Traditional Communities and Modern Cooperatives', paper to the I.D.S. Conference on Social Prerequisites for Agricultural Cooperation.

[2] J. M. Texier, 'Traditional Forms of Collective Activities', paper to the same Conference. Both papers are highly relevant. These conference papers may be published by the Institute of Development Studies in 1970 through the Manchester University Press.

---

a maternity and child welfare project, one from a settlement of young farmers, the Christian Rural Service scheme (Kigezi, Uganda), and the Rural Service Programme (Kaimosi, Kenya). The Report is published, with aid from the Rockefeller Foundation, as *New Hope for Rural Africa* (East African Publishing House for Makerere University College, Nairobi, 1969).

been specifically designed to lead ultimately to full Cooperatives.

It is obvious that voluntary agencies cannot undertake even a fiftieth part of the total task of Extension work for small farmers, although they might indeed be encouraged to do more and be supported better both by national and Aid funds. They can be especially useful in Stage I conditions, or in dry areas where a national programme does not yet exist. It is clear too that government is at a disadvantage in seeking to adopt their style. Government's technical and financial resources are greater, but a government organization cannot hope to equal the flexibility in local decision which an autonomous local agency can achieve. It could, however, move very much further in that direction.

What seems to be needed, to overcome the extreme difficulty of providing an individual Extension service to large masses of small, separate farm units, is a marriage between leadership, technical information, and management on the official side and various types of informal or pre-Cooperative activity on the farmers' side. Would it, for example, be possible, in the Indian case, to reorganize the Block so as to include an 'Agricultural Service Unit' which would offer—not demand—to take over certain types of common management functions for any sizeable group of farmers which voluntarily agreed to such a scheme, with some form of representative consultation between the farmers and the Unit? Such a scheme would certainly involve numerical strengthening of Extension staff (which is in any case necessary) and also a new element in training staff in these more managerial functions.[1] On the farmers' side, the formation of a local 'Farmers' Association', with objects and rules appropriate to the local scheme, would provide all the structure needed in the early stages.

Such a system may seem very like a Cooperative. But it differs in two vital ways. First, the management of the supply, technical advice, and primary marketing system would be provided by a reorganized and strengthened Extension unit, with a chain of higher technical and administrative reinforce-

---

[1] In fact, a mixture between the existing, but separate, forms of training for Extension and training for Cooperative Secretaries.

SUGGESTIONS, COMPARISONS, CONCLUSIONS   137

ment on call to it, in the form of the normal District staff.[1]
Secondly, it might be unnecessary to give individual issues of
crop-season credit—the standard costs of seed, spray, or
fertilizer would be deducted at the harvest stage when the crop
comes in. Credit for development of individual farms would
need separate handling, and would be subject to management
approval and supervision if it came through official sources;
farmers could, of course, be free to borrow privately for their
own farm improvement. Larger works—soil conservation,
irrigation for a group, etc.—could be treated, not as credit, but as
government investment, partly recoverable by a water rate or
similar charge.

Such a system would have an easy opportunity to develop in
one of three directions. First, into a normal Cooperative, if the
farmers' committee felt that they could do better than the
official management; in that case, the first stage would be a
'guided Cooperative' or 'pre-Cooperative'. Alternatively, into
larger Agricultural Service Units. Finally, if the system became
unnecessary as farmers became more sophisticated, incomes
rose, and private suppliers became keen to move in, it could
fade away and allow a reversion to purely individual farming,
with a relic of such common services as might still be valued.
Obviously, great care would have to be taken to see that
management costs were reasonably related to turnover, not
forgetting that at present the Extension Service is provided free
to farmers and is, in fact, a management cost borne by government but without either the power or the training to manage
in this sense.

There are quite a large number of systems which approxi-
mate to this pattern, and it would need careful formulation and
adaptation to local circumstances. The Kenya Tea Development Authority manages its thousands of small growers in
much this way—the farmers remain individuals growing their
own food or other crops but the tea crop is centrally managed.
The Fiji sugar industry, although run by a private company,
has something of this system. The Federal Land Development

---

[1] Two of the biggest and most successful Cooperative systems in East Africa (the
Kilimanjaro coffee and the Lake Victoria cotton Cooperative Unions) owe their
first success *in the early stages* to very strong management guidance from the
Administration.

Authority in Malaya runs a plantation system (rubber and palm oil) through individual 'settlers' who will one day become beneficial owners. The Gezira cotton scheme in the Sudan was partly so managed, and there are similarities with the East African tobacco system. Most of these, however, dealt primarily with a single commercial crop; such systems have not yet (to my knowledge) been widely applied to an area of mixed subsistence and cash-cropping on small holdings, nor organized by a simple variation in the normal administrative system. Perhaps the group farming system of Uganda could be adapted to this form if it were weaned both from its orthodox Cooperative structure and from its dogmatic belief in tractorized cultivation across farm boundaries. The World Bank scheme near Lilongwe in Malawi is perhaps a closer parallel. The Comilla system in East Pakistan is near to it already, in that the 'manager' of each small Primary Cooperative is in constant touch—indeed under constant training and supervision—with the Academy, and the management of the *Thana*-level Cooperative Union is strongly staffed and again closely watched and supported from the official side. Some of the 'agri-business' undertakings run by Shri Manibhai Desai near Poona, including dairying and the total transformation of a dry area by lift irrigation from a river, which retain the original cultivators in a status which might be called a guided (and financed) Cooperative, come very near to such a system, although the initiative is not from the bureaucracy but from a mixture of able individual enterprise, official loan support, and the Gandhi Memorial Trust. The Agricultural Development Corporation in Pakistan was perhaps intended to fill this role, but was pitched at a national level where it was unable to manage local groupings of farmers. ALDEV,[1] in Kenya, and the CRAD[2] system in French West Africa confined themselves mainly to technical support.

It must be made abundantly clear that these paragraphs are not put forward as a blueprint of wide immediate application. They are simply to illustrate, in the roughest form, certain things which need to be faced and certain indications of a route to success which appears to satisfy the necessary conditions. The main propositions are as follows:

[1] African Land Development Corporation.
[2] Centres Régionaux d'Agriculture et de Développement.

1. That the attempt to service millions of small farmers individually through an Extension service containing several departmental interests but without management responsibility, delivering a complex 'package' and individual cash credits, is barely feasible. It is expensive in unrecovered credit and over-complex in administrative coordination. It is likely to end up in servicing only the larger farmers who can make the system work to their advantage.

2. That the attempt to cure this by independent Cooperatives of small farmers without strengthening and supporting the Co-perative management is not only likely to fail (except where the same large farmers capture and manage it) but further complicates the administrative task by introducing an unreliable and semi-autonomous element into an already complex and confused official structure.

3. That in some areas there is little hope of advance unless someone is willing to assume management responsibility for a considerable acreage and number of farmers. In the early stages, and where this cannot easily be done by company management of a single commercial crop, it would be worth reorganizing the government service much more directly into management units for basic supply, technical service, and primary marketing, possibly abolishing the individual crop-credit system. This would require reorganization and some strengthening and retraining of the Extension staff.

4. That this would provide a stimulus and an open-ended structure which could develop later into standard Cooperatives, or into larger service units, or could revert to a much strengthened individual system.

The Extension staff in any case spend much of their time in administration, largely in administering and coordinating each other. They would need this administrative training and would use their agricultural training even more, if they were in fact taking responsibility for these substantial areas of 'guided Cooperatives', or service units. Existing training institutions could be used for retraining staff for units.

It remains to say a word concerning private enterprise on the supply side. Save in those countries which have a rooted objection to private enterprise as such, it should be able to play an increasing, and finally a dominant part in the business side of agriculture, selling fertilizer, pest-control chemicals and equipment, hand and power tools, pumps, pipes, building materials, repair and maintenance services; buying and handling produce from the primary groups; providing short-term credit to reliable customers; and seizing opportunities for processing and minor industry in the rural area as they arise. This is a stage still some way ahead in India and some other Asian countries; even further ahead in Africa. It will not be reached until the farmers' purchasing power and financial stability is much greater; but when it does come, it will immensely relieve and simplify the burden on government services, and will introduce a flexibility into farm management and farming business which, in the nature of things, government will always find it hard to achieve.

5. STAFF

Most developing countries have a large surplus of labour; many already find it hard to provide employment even for graduates of secondary schools; some have large numbers of unemployed college graduates; India has this problem even to the inclusion of engineering and agricultural university graduates. The social cost of providing government employment in agriculture for these men is certainly very low; their alternative use in the economy is likely to lie in displacing less qualified staff in much simpler jobs which do not require the heavy public investment in university education. If the result of employing them is a marked rise in agricultural productivity, the danger of an inflationary effect is not serious,[1] particularly in countries where the consumer goods industry has been working below capacity. Taxation can in any case moderate any inflationary tendency, and some form of revenue gain from increased agricultural prosperity is certainly necessary.

There is thus a *prima facie* case for increasing the agricultural field staff, on two conditions. The first is that the administrative

[1] Perhaps the most common form of inflation in developing countries is a large growth of government staff, accompanied by little or no growth in physical output. There were over 600,000 public employees in Indonesia in 1963, at a time when production was falling rapidly.

system is organized to employ them efficiently. The second—
which implies some further revenue expenditure—is that they
are equipped adequately to do a field and not an office job.
Means of transport is the most obvious equipment needed,
and studies of the cost-benefit ratio of providing Extension
staff with transport adequate to their duties are urgently
needed. There is also a question of the balance between the
higher echelons of largely administrative staff and the real
field officers.

A higher proportion of field staff would not unduly weigh
down the agricultural budget as a whole. We obtained from
five Indian State Agricultural Departments, and from the
Agricultural Department in Kenya, a rough breakdown of the
total expenditure of the Department by headings. Comparisons
cannot be made between these budgets, since the figures are
made up differently, including different functions. But each
separately shows a proportion of from 18% to 22% of the total
being spent on staff salaries and travel for the Extension side
(including HQ staff). It follows that a 50% increase in staff at
and below District level would not increase the total budget
by much over 8% (the HQ staff would be unchanged) and a
100% increase not much over 16%.[1] The proportion of such
an increase which should go to each level will differ with the
stage of development—in very early stages a large but simply
trained staff in direct contact with the village; in a transitional
stage some sacrifice of numbers to more training and expertise,
particularly on the management side; ultimately a large reduction at the lowest level and a 100% graduate staff, but well
spread out in the field. This last stage corresponds to a developed agriculture and a large private-sector contribution covering all supply, all credit, and some technical service. This
expansion would naturally be spread over some years, by reinforcing the points of progress in the way India has already
done in selecting areas for intensive effort.

There seems to be very little doubt that some such careful
restructuring of the agricultural field force, closely related to the
state of agricultural and general economic progress, would be

[1] A 16% increase in the total agricultural budget spread over five years, assuming
agriculture to represent as much as 25% of the total national budget, would
only put up this total by less than 1% per annum.

well within budgetary capacity, could pay high dividends, and would also allow for restructuring the career pattern within the field force. After a large increase in initial intake to increase total size, largely at the middle and lower levels, the long-term tendency would be for the force to shrink in total numbers but to rise in average salary and in the proportion of higher posts, and this should allow for an adequate promotion ratio.

6. ADMINISTRATION

A good deal of the discussion in earlier chapters has revolved round the perennial problem of keeping government staff from several different Departments and specialisms so carefully in step that a complicated package of programmes can be delivered to a multitude of individual farmers with a high degree of accuracy. This problem is at its worst in the earliest stages, when the smaller farmers can do little for themselves, the private sector is undeveloped at village level, and Cooperatives of small farmers are too weak in managerial capacity and resources to keep their end up in the system. It is obvious, from this very list of difficulties, that time and success will tend to cure all three of these, and almost simultaneously. The farmers will become stronger, the private sector will expand, the Cooperatives will do their job more effectively with stronger and better-educated membership and more financial resources.

Nevertheless, the early stages are still with us in a great number of developing countries and in some areas of nearly all of them.

Outside the administrative structure itself, the three main suggestions made here emphasize especially an enabling rather than a prescriptive attitude. The first, and most important, is enabling by investment—in India, by water supply and drainage above all, in Africa possibly by clearance and land-shaping which will be critical in some areas, although there is still much scope for better water control;[1] but the nature of the investment needed naturally differs widely. The second, an enabling attitude in Extension, rather than target-fixing—it is the farmers,

---

[1] Groundwater tends to be deeper in the African plateau than in the huge plains of India/Pakistan which lie south of the Himalayas and in the great river valleys of S.E. Asia.

not the staff, who decree what targets can be reached. The third, the provision of certain common management services in some form of 'guided Cooperative' or service unit.

However, there will still remain for long enough the problem of internal administrative coordination. An important reduction in this is to reduce component agencies, where possible. I have brutally suggested that great caution should be used in creating a mass of weak Cooperatives and then entrusting them with key functions which, if unfulfilled, disorganize the whole system; the same may apply to weak or corrupt representative bodies wherever their prime interest is politics rather than development. This does, however, mean that the total load on direct administration is increased temporarily, though it will have more control.

As to the administration itself, in a great many countries the cream of the administrative staff has been concentrated in the Provincial and District Administration, and the focus of power and prestige lies with it. In the early stages of development this steel framework cannot be dispensed with as an essential co-ordinating and invigorating force in the field. The time when it can give way altogether to representative all-purpose local government is still far ahead in most peasant countries. However, the very high prestige of the Administration all too easily implies too low a rating of the technical services. This is unfortunate in a development context; below the D.C. himself, the interference of junior Administration or Revenue staff should be cut down.

Secondly, a clearer and simpler grouping of administrative services might be helpful. The three key functions are agriculture, animal husbandry, and fisheries; engineering;[1] and supply —credit—marketing. At District level these three divisions should certainly be able to command enough ability to be self-administering, under the overall coordination of the D.C. himself. The separation of commercial services from the two technical divisions is of especial importance.

It seems logical also to separate Community Development Departments more clearly from this trio of development services. In very backward areas for which no major develop-

---

[1] Includes agricultural engineering, roads, building, water (irrigation and domestic), drainage.

ment effort is devised, Community Development may be the main field influence, with a call on technical help where it is needed; but at a later stage, when the main effort is to break through the barrier of poverty, Community Development should be gradually merging into normal education, health, and social services which have their own Departments. The historical fact that Community Development and Panchayati Raj were the leading influences in the India of the 1950s is already causing some confusion in the new development effort which has gathered strength since 1960.

Further, the concept of a 'Project Officer' needs to be very cautiously used. This title, as used in I.A.D.P. parlance, is a misnomer when applied to an officer who is in fact charged with coordinating virtually the whole range of farmer-oriented activities in a District of over a million population. It can be useful for fairly small and self-contained specific projects (such as the Mwea/Tebere rice scheme in Kenya, or many similar settlement or irrigation 'projects'),[1] and then usually in their early organizational stages, before they sink into the landscape of general economic activity, subject to the general norm of administration. The D.C. himself can be the only Project Officer for a District as a whole, and he does not need this title. If he needs senior assistance, the officer concerned should be in a 'staff' not a 'line' relationship to him. In so far as the D.C. is increasingly relieved of revenue and magisterial functions, he becomes more easily a development leader. We are thus left at the (Indian) District level—the appropriate level would have different names in different countries—with a trio of vital functions: one representing the whole range of agricultural, animal husbandry, and veterinary services; one the engineering and works function; and one the whole business function of supply, credit, and marketing, with the D.C. as chairman of the group and with staff officers or specialists in support, including fishery or forestry men where needed. In a very advanced stage, a small planning unit might be an excellent innovation.

Two major questions still present difficulty. First, there is the

---

[1] For a recent analysis of the administration of settlement schemes in tropical Africa, in which the Mwea/Tebere scheme is used as a case-study, see Robert Chambers, *Settlement Schemes in Tropical Africa* (Routledge & Kegan Paul, London, 1969).

problem coordination nearer to the field—at Block level or its equivalent. Indian experience, which has been the most comprehensive and experimental, suggests that this lower focus is highly valuable, for its accessibility and immediacy of knowledge. It also suggests that direct administrative *control* by a single officer of technical staff and operations at this level causes gradually increasing friction as the development programme gains momentum and complexity. To put in, *ex officio*, an Administration/Revenue officer at this level as coordinator offends against the increasingly technical emphasis in development. A possible alternative is to create a special cadre of 'Development Officers', selected in roughly equal proportions from experienced field staff in each of the three main functions, and specially trained for a job as coordinating chairmen. Their line of responsibility would be to the D.C. in his development role, and their career structure would include either promotion to the D.C.'s staff or back to a higher grade in their own Department. Their role as Block leaders would not give them actual control of technical staff, and obstinate departmental differences would have to be resolved at District level. Except in the last respect, and for a greater emphasis on professional training, this position is very close to that of the B.D.O.; but the difference is vital.

The second difficulty lies in the scope and control of the business function, in stages before private suppliers, banks, good Cooperatives, and an effective merchanting system can be expected to carry this load. The type of training needed to carry out this function is, to say the least, uncommon in the civil service—it is probably for this reason that government has attempted to farm it out to Cooperatives, banks, or public corporations. But experience shows that the resulting weakness in coordination between the production (agriculture and engineering) and the business function can be nearly fatal to the package philosophy. The government Cooperative Department and its staff have more knowledge and training in this field than anyone in the field administration; if it was not so tied to Co-operatives of standard form as a sole method, it might well be used, blossoming into a Department of Supply, Credit, and Marketing, with a free choice of agency appropriate to local circumstances and stages of growth.

Such a Department would have to use an extremely wide range of method. In areas where the cash economy is weak, it would have to be prepared to organize direct supply, credit, and purchasing. In more advanced conditions, it could use contracts or licensed agencies, or Cooperatives where they are strong enough. By agreements within the commercial banking system it might well have to take responsibility for direct credit schemes, again with the ultimate aim of shedding the load as and when borrowers became more stable and sophisticated. Most of such policy decisions would have to be made at national level where major suppliers or banks were concerned, and the field staff would be concerned partly with execution but also partly with monitoring the agency arrangements. The Supply-Credit-Marketing Officer at District or Block level would in any case be the contact to whom the agricultural and engineering staff would turn for action on all these subjects.

Here again, some Indian States have got very close to such a system. To give one example, the following is the procedure for financing fairly expensive types of tube-well irrigation schemes in Madhya Pradesh. First, the Agricultural field staff suggest an area which is thought suitable. The geologist (from the all-India Geological Survey Department at Nagpur) does a survey. On the basis of this the Agriculture Department and Tube-well Directorate draw up a scheme for, say, a hundred wells. This goes to the Agriculture Refinance Corporation, a government-established consortium of banks, under the wing of the Cooperative Department. The Agriculture Department has a liaison officer stationed in the A.R.C. office and a further expert survey of the scheme is then carried out for detailed engineering and economic assessment. After final approval by the Registrar of Cooperatives and the Director of Agriculture, the Directorate of Tube-wells executes the work for the farmers (against loan applications from them), and is paid direct by the banks. Recovery from the farmers concerned is nil in the first year, interest only in the second year, and interest plus repayment instalments in subsequent years. This (elaborate) system shows in detail the interlock between the trio of agriculturalists, engineers, and the business side in getting water to the right place at the right price and in recovery of the cost from the beneficiaries. It is interesting that the Cooperative Department is here acting well outside its usual supervision of standard Cooperatives and of standard Cooperative banks.

The number of variants which a Supply-Credit-Marketing Department might need to use is very great. What is important is to relieve the agronomic and engineering staff of these business functions (so that a trained Agricultural Extension Officer does not spend inordinate time filling up loan application forms); to avoid using Cooperatives as a *standard* tool; to accept responsibility for direct action where the private commercial sector or Cooperatives are too weak to carry it effectively; and to shed it again when either of them, and the farmers themselves, have reached a stage when government action is no longer needed.

To complete this analysis of administration at field levels, a word is needed on the staffing and administration of the Agricultural Service Units for small farmers suggested earlier in this chapter. The trio of representatives at Block level would need to approve the outlines of each such scheme; but an additional Extension Officer, perhaps legitimately called a 'Local Project Officer' (or Secretary), would be needed for each scheme on the ground, working closely with the Farmers' Association, but referring for aid and guidance to the Block. It is here that additional field staff would be needed, and here that a career opportunity for the best and most energetic junior Extension staff would be found.

7. THE DEMOCRATIC ELEMENT

The analysis of previous chapters has suggested some fairly clear lines of distinction in the use of democratic systems as an aid to development. The most important of these is to separate actual participation in development programmes (village level) and consultation or criticism (Block level) from civic and political training in delegated administration, i.e. representative Local Government. It may be possible, in very sophisticated areas such as Maharashtra, to delegate the development function, as distinct from routine administration of roads, education, health, etc., to representative Local Government. Even if this is the case, a District Panchayat or County Council would have to be able to distinguish its role as an elected representative body and an arena of political action from its role in using local panchayats (or 'Development Committees' or whatever their local name may be) for the purpose of participation or consultation. In practice it is hardly conceivable that such a distinction would be observed. If the major body at District is political, politics will certainly run down through the minor units.

India is in some ways a highly sophisticated country, and yet it still has plenty of difficulties in Local Government. Most of the evidence from the establishment of County Councils or parallel bodies in tropical Africa has also been extremely discouraging; various combinations of corruption, bankruptcy, and political extremism have marked their career. Some of the reasons for this have been suggested elsewhere.[1] It is for this reason that in this study, which has agricultural development as its central theme, the use of elected councils for development purposes at any level above the Block has been treated with extreme suspicion. At present, indeed, the problems of co-ordinating development effort to multitudes of small farmers by direct administrative means have proved more than sufficiently complex and difficult, and many of them are still unsolved. Until they are better under control, and the essential strategies and methods are generally much clearer, it would seem merely foolhardy to introduce another erratic and uncontrollable agency into the field. Moreover, if government itself is trying to support some kind of restructuring of local economic and social power in favour of the smaller men and the younger progressives, it may well be better to start this process through direct administrative help to them. At a later stage, when they are more able to stand on their own feet, they would be more able to assert themselves through elected bodies, in which at present the privileged groups are bound to be strongly entrenched. There are fine balances of political judgment and development policy here.

Purely as participation, the village and Block councils must be regarded as a success. Although lethargic in some cases, overawed by the traditional leaders in others, the councils have provided a window to the outer world—though often a very small and dusty one—for tens of thousands of villages. They have brought a new aspect of government into touch with the

---

[1] G. Hunter, *Modernizing Peasant Societies* (O.U.P., London, 1969).

rural area and new visions of development. They have elicited at least some new leadership and put some new resources behind the agricultural effort.

Certainly, the real element of progressiveness lies in the professional staff at Block and District level, who can bring new opportunity to the farmer. Provided that this staff continue to work impartially as far as they can—and this implies some independence from purely local and political pressures—the smaller farmers have a new ally, and need not regard the Block council as a way of reinforcing the power of the already powerful. On the contrary, they have a footing to approach their elected leaders which they did not have before.

8.   CONCLUSION

This study of Indian agricultural administration has been concerned with a very elaborate system. There are dozens of countries where not a quarter of the thought or resources has been given to this field—countries where a relatively weak Agricultural Department is struggling ineffectively with a traditional farming system, where the problem of coordination has barely been posed, much less settled, where both research and investment are clearly inadequate. The purpose of taking this elaborate model is not to recommend it to all countries. It is rather to suggest to those many countries now genuinely seeking agricultural development what complexities and blind alleys in administrative policy may lie ahead of them, and to help them to avoid the worst of the pitfalls. It has been assumed that a central object of government policy will be to extend the opportunity of advance to the majority, and not merely to a favoured minority of farmers; and this assumption has made the task of organization more difficult, even if the ultimate reward in both political and economic terms may be greater.

Perhaps the most constantly recurring theme of this book has been the need for adaptation of policy and structures to the movement and change in society, as it passes at quite local levels from poverty, and a traditional adaptation to poverty, towards greater individual prosperity and a stronger cash-economy. It is seen as a transition from necessary and multiple intervention by government to break the circle of dependence and powerlessness to a condition where the farmer, in his greater security, can choose among the richer variety of services which a richer economy can offer, and thus 'coordinate' his own farm-management by himself. The most difficult part of this transition, as an administrative problem, is the earliest stage, where government, possibly weak in personnel and in a poor society, has to assume the maximum task. For in these early stages even the agencies which later on will share that task—Cooperatives, Local Government—are composed largely either of the weak and poor for whom the help is needed, or of the rich and powerful whose position often stands in the way of a wider progress.

The Indian Government has tried to shoulder this task of intervention. But—and this is the second main theme—in seeing it as a task of prescription rather than of enablement, and in setting detailed targets beyond what it has the real power to achieve, it has created an administrative system so complex that it is constantly tripped up in its own tangle, and so rigid that the highly local needs of farmers and the discretions of the Extension staff are excluded. Moreover, it is a system which cannot easily reach more than a small proportion of beneficiaries; indeed, only this small proportion have the means and power to exploit it. Finally, in an intention to move at once to what may be a second stage of the transition, it has endeavoured to use cooperative and democratic agencies prematurely, before either their staff or the political environment in which they work is good enough to give a fair chance of success.

If India can barely make such a system work satisfactorily, it is unlikely that other countries, less sophisticated in leadership and less rich in the variety of private enterprise and varied skills, will be able to do even as well. It has therefore become the main object of this book to suggest how the task can be simplified and the administrative strain reduced. It is just as useless to expect miracles from government as to expect them from the farmer.

It is impossible to close this study of Extension without reference to the long, patient task which the ordinary field officers, from the lowest to the highest, have been carrying out over so many years and in so many countries all over the developing world. They have worked surrounded by frustrations—by lack of the investment which would have so greatly helped them; by inadequate research, which has so often led to local failures; and by a tangle of administration which be-devils their efforts in so many ways. Yet the fact that farming does break through, here and there, with notable success is due more than anything to the long process of education and help which they have tried to give to the farmer. When the new crop or the new water supply comes, it may seem to have been sole cause of the success. But it is the *last* decisive cause in a long history of preparation which has made the farmers able to grasp and exploit opportunity. Many opportunities have, in fact, been available in the past; but they were not grasped be-cause this groundwork had not yet been completed. Patience and persistence seldom get their due of reward and praise: it has certainly been earned by these men and women who have worked, for a very moderate reward, in the heat or the cold, to make the small cumulative improvements which at last are leading to great results. Nowhere is this tribute better deserved than by the staff who work in India's villages.

Finance for Panchayats in Madras State

1. Local cess (levied at 45 paise per rupee of land revenue).
2. Local cess surcharge (fixed by Panchayat Union Council).
3. Local cess surcharge matching grant: released as per classification of Block.
4. Surcharge on Entertainment Tax and Show Tax.
5. Grants for Elementary Education:
    (a) Land Revenue Assignment: released at Rs.1 per capita.
    (b) Local Education Grant: released as per classification of Block.
    (c) Supplementary Education Grant: released at 18% on ordinary expenditure.
    (d) Special D.A. Grant: the deficit due to enhancement of D.A. given as grant.
6. Local Roads Grant: released at 40 paise per capita.
7. Local Irrigation Grant: full grant.
8. Grants for Development works:
    (a) Agriculture, Animal Husbandry, and Fisheries: Rs.2 lakhs for 5 years;
    (b) Village Works Grant: Rs.2 lakhs to Rs.4 lakhs for 5 years;
    (c) School Building Grant: Rs.15 for school place created;
    (d) Social Education Grant: 10 paise per capita per year;
    (e) Women and Child Welfare Grant: $33\frac{1}{3}$ paise per capita for 5 years;
    (f) Grants for Rural Arts and Crafts, etc.: Rs.50,000 for 5 years;
    (g) Maternity and Child Welfare Grant: $\frac{2}{3}$ of gross expenditure is given as grant;
    (h) Grants for Dispensaries: $\frac{2}{3}$ of expenditure is given as grant.

REVENUE FOR VILLAGE PANCHAYATS

(a) House Tax
(b) Vehicle Tax
(c) Profession Tax
(d) Local cess
(e) Surcharge on Stamp Duty
(f) Entertainment Tax
(g) House Tax Matching Grant

LOANS ALLOTMENT (BLOCKS)

(a) New Well Subsidy Scheme	Rs.30 lakhs
(b) Pumpset Scheme	Rs.29 lakhs
(c) Intensive Manuring Scheme	Rs.30 lakhs
(d) A.L. L.I.L. Act	Rs. 6 lakhs
House Tax Demand	Rs.19 lakhs
Profession Tax Demand	Rs. 3 lakhs
Vehicle Tax Demand	Rs. 3 lakhs

The Blocks are classified as A, B, C, D, and grants are released according to classification.

Note: 100 paise=1 rupee: 100,000 rupees=1 lakh. D.A.=Dearness Allowance (i.e. Cost of Living).

Note on the Agricultural University, Jabalpur

Extract from Notes taken at Jabalpur Agricultural University
A meeting is held with the Director of Agriculture and the field staff before the sowing season to finalize the package of practices, etc. Each of the six Colleges in the University has a Block attached to it for Extension work (and to provide a two-way traffic).

About 1,500 farmers have been trained on short courses, e.g., courses for the high-yielding varieties and the new hybrids, plant-protection, repair of pumps, vegetable growing, maintenance of tractors, poultry-keeping, maintenance of a dairy herd, kitchen gardening, fruit preservation. Training is also done for the Agriculture Department Extension staff—one-month courses of 50 at a time; also the senior staff for four or five days for up-to-date information.

The University staff subject-matter specialists also go to villages where the farmers can easily assemble, within a radius of twenty-five miles from the University campus.

The University staff are also providing communication material: the V.L.W.s get some information sheets and are encouraged to ask questions—the answers being given in a circulated news-sheet. There is also a fortnightly circular letter which goes to every Extension Officer and to senior staff. There are periodical bulletins, e.g., forecasts of the weather or of pests. Also a feature in Hindi—four to five times every month: about two hundred have been given in the last two years. The University plans to set up its own printing press in the next few months—there are American advisers working on this now: Home Science, Agriculture, and Veterinary College staff will work on it and there will be a page for the women working on Extension. Articles of topical interest in the local newspapers are also used. Every Sunday, from 6.30 to 6.45 p.m., there is a radio programme of topical interest with a quiz at the end—answers are invited and the best gets a prize of Rs.20. (Four hundred replies are generally received.) The University is trying to get a 15-minute period before this programme starts for Extension subjects.

There is a liaison committee with the Agriculture Department, of which the Vice-Chancellor is chairman; the Secretary for Agriculture, the Director of Agriculture, and the Joint Directors, with the Deans of the University working on Extension, are members. This meeting is held once in three months. The Vice-Chancellor and Deans report the views of the other Colleges in the University too.

There is a proposal to send fifteen V.L.W.s to the University every year for a degree course (three years instead of the usual four), but only those with science matric. and five years' service would be taken. It is not yet known whether a rise in rank would follow.

The Extension staff in the University are the Director of Extension plus two Joint Directors with subject-matter specialists borrowed from the various Departments; these give one-third of their time to teaching, one-third to research, and one-third to Extension. There are ten of these at each campus, and the associated Dean coordinates their work. There is also an Extension wing or Department, with a Dean and two lecturers, in each College.

The education of farming women is done by Home Science graduates (women) who have extra training in Extension. Between ten and fifteen farming families using high-yielding varieties and hybrids are adopted and helped. One or two women teachers on each campus also organize Mahila Mandals and work through them.

'The Madhya Pradesh Organisation of Progressive Farmers' is a group of voluntary rural leaders between the ages of 17 and 35. There have been two courses in the University per year for them. The members must each adopt two cultivators—'each one teach two'. A similar group of 8–18-year-olds is being organized on the lines of the 4H Clubs in California—rearing poultry, etc.—but this is only in course of being started. Next year the University may organize a group of over-35s.

There is an Apprenticeship Scheme under which promising university students are employed as Extension Agents—there were ten in the first year, rising to fifteen and then twenty per year. The first year's trial worked very well. The apprentices are paid Rs.225 p.m. They live in the farmer's house (single room with furniture) though they make their own arrangements for food.

Index

Adutarai, 102

Afghanistan, 119

African Land Development Corporation (ALDEV), Kenya, 138

Agricultural Colleges, 53, 54, 57

Agricultural Development Corporation, Pakistan, 37, 138

— — Officers, in Maharashtra, 45

— Extension Officers (A.E.O.s), 52, 53, 54–5, 58, 64–5, 72, 82, 86, 88, 94, 98–99, 118, 142, 155

— — Service, 9, 14–15, 25, 30, 31–8, 40, 52–5, 57–8, 61, 62, 64, 65, 68–70, 81, 84–5, 88–9, 90, 92, 97, 98, 101, 104–5, 118–19, 131, 136, 139–40, 142–3, 147, 150–1

— Finance Corporations, 38, 39, 80

— Refinance Corporation, Madhya Pradesh, 146

— Service Units, 136–7, 139, 147

— Universities, 30, 52–3, 54, 55, 57–8, 84–9, 90, 102, 104, 155–6

Aligarh, 89, 95

ammonium sulphate, 94

Amritsar, 93

Anand Extension Education Institute, 54

Andhra Pradesh, 15, 34, 35, 43, 45, 46, 47, 57, 72, 87, 111, 117

animal husbandry, 28, 31, 33, 41, 49, 55, 72, 85, 89, 106, 143, 144, 153

animateurs, in 'French' Africa, 72

Applied Nutrition Programme, 49, 109–10

artificial insemination for cattle, 49, 110, 115

Assam, 15, 23, 42, 98

bajra (millet), 95

Balvantrai Mehta report (1957), 26

Banaras, 66

Bangalore Agricultural University, 57, 87

banks, 38, 39, 126, 145, 146

Bareilly, 89

Baroda, 63

Bengal, West, 10, 15, 23

Bhopal, 105

Bhor, 46

Bhubaneswar Agricultural University, 55, 57, 87

Bihar, 15, 23, 34, 57, 82, 99, 104, 116

Block Development Officers (B.D.O.s), 24, 25, 27, 31, 33, 35, 36, 40, 42–3, 45, 53, 54, 63, 73, 111, 116

— panchayats, 25, 27, 41, 42–4, 45, 46–7, 73, 75, 108–9, 111, 112, 114, 115–16, 117, 148–9, 154

— Panchayat Union, Madras, 35, 47, 74

Blocks, 15, 24–6, 27, 28, 31–6, 39, 42–3, 45, 46, 51, 52, 54–5, 69–70, 73–4, 84–5, 91, 92, 97, 100, 101, 147

bore-wells, 39, 102, 106

Borgo a Mozzano, Italy, 64–5

British, 20, 69, 71

Budaun, 89

Buganda, 119 (*see* Uganda)

canals, 23, 39, 65, 96

caste, 24, 41, 44, 79, 114, 115, 117, 129

cattle-purchase, 39, 49

Chattrapatti, 46

coconuts, 10, 24

coffee, 131, 137

Coimbatore, 57, 102

Collectors, 25, 27, 31, 33, 34–5, 37, 45, 56, 111, 117 (*see* Deputy Commissioners; District Magistrates)

Comilla, 138

community development, 33, 43, 47, 108–10

Community Development Departments, 24–5, 26–7, 28, 33, 36, 40, 143–4

Congo, 113

Cooperative Departments, 55, 145, 146–7

Cooperatives, 9, 10, 24–5, 31, 38–9, 42, 54, 55, 63, 73–4, 75, 76, 77–8, 79–80, 90, 99, 101, 102, 103, 111, 117, 128–9, 133, 134, 135, 137, 139, 142, 143, 145, 146, 150

corn, 93

cotton, 77, 81, 137–8

credit, 9, 13, 28, 38–9, 51, 61, 67, 71, 73, 75, 76, 77–8, 80, 85, 90, 92, 94, 97, 99–100, 132, 134, 137, 139, 140, 143, 144, 146 (*see* Loans)

crops, 14, 26, 30, 35, 49, 52, 57, 65–6, 67, 68, 71, 76, 83, 88, 93–4, 95–6, 97, 102, 104, 115, 130, 155 (*see* plant breeding; plant protection)

dairies, 77, 135, 138, 155